The Challenge of Change

The Challenge of Change

Putting Patients before Providers

Brendan Drumm

ORPEN PRESS

Published by Orpen Press
Lonsdale House
Avoca Avenue
Blackrock
Co. Dublin
Ireland

e-mail: info@orpenpress.com
www.orpenpress.com

ISBN: 978-1-871305-26-5

A catalogue record for this book is available from the British Library.

Printed in Ireland by Colorman Ltd.

About the Author

Brendan Drumm was born in Manorhamilton, Co. Leitrim. In his early teenage years, his family moved to Sligo, where he attended secondary school at Summerhill College. He undertook his undergraduate medical education at the National University of Ireland, Galway. Following this, he emigrated to Canada for postgraduate training in paediatrics and was subsequently appointed as a paediatric gastroenterologist at The Hospital for Sick Children in Toronto and assistant professor at the University of Toronto.

Having spent almost a decade in Canada, he returned to Ireland, and in 1991 he was appointed as professor and head of the Department of Paediatrics at University College Dublin, and Paediatric Gastroenterologist at Our Lady's Children's Hospital in Dublin. He established a research unit that is recognised internationally as a leader in the area of paediatric gastroenterology.

His research work has been published on several occasions in many of the world's leading medical journals, including the *New England Journal of Medicine*, *The Lancet*, the *Journal of Clinical Investigation*, *Gastroenterology* and *Proceedings of the National Academy of Sciences*. He is a fellow of the Royal College of Physicians in Ireland, Canada and the UK, as well as being a fellow of the American Gastroenterological Association.

In 2005, he was appointed for a five-year term as the first chief executive officer of the Health Service Executive, an organisation established by the Irish Government to manage the delivery of all health and personal social services in Ireland.

Acknowledgements

Achieving change requires a core of people who are committed to making things better, and have the courage and tenacity to lead their colleagues in a new direction. From directors of nursing to human resource managers, from procurement managers to consultants, from chefs to social workers, from general practitioners to physiotherapists, from caring receptionists to psychologists, I had the privilege to work with such people all across Ireland. Some were working in a group of two or three, while others were part of huge departments. They could have waited to see what would transpire but instead chose to lead the change in their area, big or small. They could have sat back and criticised, but instead they chose to fix the problems.

These people know who they are. They will never be recognised, nor, indeed, do they seek recognition. They are the unsung heroes, whose only interest is in improving services for the communities they serve. As I travelled across this country for five years, I found their commitment both humbling and inspiring.

Without these people nothing worthwhile could be achieved.

PREFACE

Dr Eamon Ralph, who is the general practitioner in the village of Kildysart in Co. Clare, speaks of the wonderful privilege it is to practise medicine. Eamon has spent almost all of his professional life working in rural communities in the West of Ireland, which can require him to be available on an almost continuous basis. He describes this privilege as being in a position to offer relief or consolation to people who are ill or vulnerable.

All healthcare professionals are similarly privileged. Most who us who undertake a career in healthcare do so because we want to be able to support those who are ill. However, despite this commitment to our individual patients, we often continue to provide care using processes that can make life very difficult for those who need our services. The privilege that has been given to us must also be seen as coming with a responsibility to change.

This book outlines a change or transformation programme focused on developing a healthcare service capable of providing care for patients in as seamless a way as possible. Creating such an integrated service is a major aspiration for most developed countries, but very few have achieved it.

The book is about the challenge of systemic change in general, change within a public service environment and, perhaps most demanding of all, change in a health service that operates in a public service environment. As such, the book is for members of the public – the taxpayers who fund the health system and should demand a quality service – managers, clinicians, politicians, and those interested in change and governance.

I have written this book for a number of reasons. First, I hope that, having read this book, members of the public might accept that they have to insist that the healthcare service is structured and operates in a manner that ensures the easiest possible access to services, and that their care is delivered in the most effective and efficient way possible. Second, I hope that clinicians will accept that it is our responsibility to lead the implementation of the changes that are required to achieve this. Finally, I hope that the reader may get some insights into why achieving worthwhile change in a public sector environment is slow and often unpopular.

While change in any environment is difficult, healthcare systems are notoriously resistant to change. Because of this, the temptation is to avoid significant change and instead to try and obtain improvement by investing more in the existing systems. Such an approach can be quite successful in dealing with issues like waiting lists in the short term. However, the long-term benefits are unlikely to be substantial, as services continue to be organised so that the patient has to navigate from one point to another in the system.

In 2005, Ireland was not only persisting with but expanding historic systems of providing care. The alternative was to transform the way healthcare services were provided. Following its establishment, the HSE immediately set about undertaking such a transformation. This book outlines the major components of, as well as the challenges faced by, the HSE's transformation programme, which was initiated in 2006. These included developing clinical leaders to play a central role in leading the transformation, initiating a major reconfiguration of the hospital system, developing a culture of working in multidisciplinary teams rather than working in professional silos, developing a performance measurement and management system, and reducing our expenditure, especially in high-spend areas such as pharmaceuticals. The overall management structure for the health service had to be completely reconfigured by merging the hospital and community services into one operational structure with a single management system.

Resistance to a change programme of this nature and scale is always going to be significant. This is especially the case in the health service, where stakeholders affected by the change vary from the general public to politicians, major contractors such as pharmaceutical companies, and powerful representative organisations for professional groups such as doctors and nurses. It was critical for everybody involved in this change programme to understand that bringing about change in a public sector environment was not going to be universally popular. It would require both courage and tenacity from the many managers and clinicians who were committed to improving services for the public.

Is progress being made? The health service budget in Ireland had increased from €3.7 billion annually in 1997 to €11.5 billion in 2005. Despite this, in 2006, the Euro Health Consumer Index (EHCI) ranked Ireland as number twenty-five out of twenty-six European countries assessed in terms of the quality of their health service, based on 2005 outcomes. By 2009, the last year for which reporting is, as yet, available, Ireland had achieved thirteenth place among the thirty-three countries now included in the EHCI. During this same period, Ireland has dramatically improved the value for money it is obtaining for expenditure on health services, and the health services have operated within budget each year. The EHCI, commenting in their 2009 report on Ireland's improving performance, stated: 'The creation of the Health Service Executive was obviously a much-needed reform.' Developing a modern integrated healthcare service is a difficult journey, especially for those who work in the health services, but these annual assessments indicate that we are travelling in the right direction.

I had an interesting experience just as this book was about to go to print. I spoke at a conference in Dublin about clinical leadership and its role in change. Following my presentation, I was approached by a number of people who were complimentary about what I had said, but some of whom expressed disappointment that I had not outlined a similar vision of change during my time as CEO of the HSE. This surprised me, as the talk on change that I had just given was essentially the same one I had given several times a week, up and down the country, during my five years as CEO of the HSE. I had even used the same stories, which are again used in this book, outlining the differences between how health services operate as compared to other services. I went back to look at the transcript of the Michael Littleton Memorial lecture, which I had given on national radio in 2006, one year after becoming CEO, which again differed little from what I had just delivered at this recent conference.

It is impossible for me to know why some people's perception of what I say has changed so much. Is it that I am now outlining a transformation programme that has taken root, rather than trying to convince people to initiate change? Is it that Ireland is now in the middle of an economic crisis and therefore change is more acceptable? Is it because I am now speaking as a commentator rather than as CEO of the HSE, and therefore people who work in healthcare are less affected by my discussing change?

Or perhaps the answer lies in the following statement by the German philosopher Arthur Schopenhauer (1788–1860): 'All truth passes through three stages. First, it is ridiculed. Second, it is violently opposed. Third, it is accepted as being self-evident.'

Contents

Introduction

The Transformation Programme

The person who approached me in 2004 about the role of chief executive officer (CEO) in the Health Service Executive (HSE), the new company established to manage the Irish health service, was Ellen Roche from PricewaterhouseCoopers. As Ellen discussed the position with me, she became interested in my view that the Irish healthcare system needed radical transformation. However, at our second or third meeting she raised a significant concern. She pointed out that for the previous twenty-five years I had worked as a paediatrician, a rewarding career in which your care is highly valued by parents and children. She was concerned that the job I was considering as CEO of the HSE would move me to the opposite end of a spectrum, as the organisation would be frequently exposed to much criticism in the media. Her concern was that it would be impossible for me to make such an adjustment. At the same time, many friends expressed the view that this was an impossible job for anyone to succeed in.

I fully accepted the view that this job and the HSE were going to attract attention, much of which would not be favourable. Implementing changes that really make a difference, especially in a public sector environment, is almost always going to be unpopular. However, this organisation had not only an opportunity, but also, in my view, a responsibility to radically change the way in which health services were provided. The HSE was going to achieve very little of consequence for people in Ireland if its focus was on being popular.

For several years, I had believed that the way healthcare services were provided in Ireland, in common with many other systems in developed countries, had to be changed if we were to provide the best possible care for patients. The changes required would meet resistance and could only be achieved if the process of change was led by clinicians, doctors, nurses and therapists from across the professional groups. Most clinicians work very hard for individual patients and their families. However, we often do not take responsibility for trying to improve the overall service. The way the healthcare system works affects everybody, and if it is badly planned or underperforming the consequences for the whole population are immense. It is surely the responsibility of clinicians to contribute to improving the wider service in the same way as they commit to helping their individual patients.

Accepting the need for radical changes in any system is extremely difficult, especially for those of us who have worked in a service for many years. In 2005, healthcare professionals interviewed in the media seldom proposed any change in how services were provided. Most usually claimed that the system was good but overworked. Proposals to improve services for the public generally revolved around investing more money to provide more services, using the existing structures and processes. If the public continued to accept the populist view that the problems in our health service were largely due to a lack of money, health service staff were unlikely to identify that the care provided could be dramatically improved by changing the way we worked.

Therefore, as I undertook the role of CEO, I continually stated that the Irish healthcare system was adequately funded. This was both unexpected and controversial as health service management and clinicians historically blamed insufficient funding for the problems affecting the Irish healthcare system. This to some extent allowed everyone to avoid taking any responsibility for improving the service. Media analysis generally supported the view that underfunding was the major problem because Ireland spent less money than some other Western European countries on healthcare. However, most commentators ignored the fact that Ireland should have been spending far less than many European countries as a much smaller proportion of its population was over 65 years of age, which is the age group that accounts for the bulk of healthcare expenditure.

From my perspective, the problem was that services were more often than not provided in a way that primarily facilitated those us professionals who provided the services rather than the patient. Investing more money to provide more of the same was therefore not necessarily the best solution. However, while the establishment of the HSE created a new organisational structure, it was unclear what difference this structural change was going to make for service users.

Simply creating a single organisation which would continue to deliver frontline services in the same way as before was not something that was going to serve any useful function for the people of Ireland. A transformation agenda focused on changing the way services were provided had already been outlined for two areas. In mental health, the 2005 report *A Vision for Change* outlined a radical and exciting change programme to improve the quality of mental health services in Ireland. The National Cancer Forum report, *A Strategy for Cancer Control in Ireland,* launched in 2006, outlined clearly how cancer services needed to be reconfigured in Ireland. These were both published as comprehensive transformation plans and are not dealt with further in this book.

We now needed to develop a transformation plan for the whole of the health service if the creation of the HSE was to mean anything. The fundamental goal of the transformation programme is to create an integrated model of care where patients receive most of their care in their own community and move seamlessly between services (Chapter 1). This involved changing the Irish healthcare system from its traditional focus on hospitals to developing community-based services delivered by multidisciplinary teams. Hospitals were historically established to deal with acute events, such as patients with serious infections and patients requiring gall bladder surgery or surgery for appendicitis or perforated ulcers. After treatment the patient returned home. In the first half of the twentieth century, acute illness accounted for most of the work of healthcare services. We now live in an era when people live much longer, and the management of chronic disease, such as diabetes, heart failure or chronic lung disease, is the major demand on our health services. Unfortunately, over the last thirty to forty years, as this change in demand has occurred, we have continued to use hospital-based systems designed for treating acute and emergency presentations to care for the huge numbers of patients with chronic disease. Most of these hospital-based processes are inappropriate for the task and it is unfair to subject people with a chronic disease to such processes. Management of chronic disease demands that professionals from various disciplines work together in community-based primary care teams and that hospitals engage with such teams in planning and providing care outside the hospital setting. Creating an integrated system that provides services in this way is a major journey of change.

The alternative was to continue fixing pieces of the system. Investing more money in individual services, for example diabetes or heart surgery, can greatly improve services for that group of patients. However, if the investment is simply providing more of the same service, the overall gains for the public are limited because the underlying healthcare system remains unchanged. Under such circumstances, each of these areas requires significant investment to bring about and maintain improvements and yet they individually represent relatively small components of the total healthcare system. Fixing the overall system piecemeal like this, based on retaining our existing work practices, would be impossible in terms of the investment required, and ultimately this system would be unsustainable.

The first thing you are told when planning a change or transformation programme is that the majority of such programmes fail. For reasons described in Chapter 15, transformation programmes in the public sector are more likely to fail than in the private sector, and even in the private sector many struggle to achieve their goal. The HSE could have been considered to be facing an impossible task. Not only was it just established as a new organisation, which involved amalgamating many existing large organisations – a considerable challenge in its own right – but it was seeking at the same time to completely transform the way in which health services were provided in Ireland. You could, however, take an alternative view, which is that the amalgamation of the existing services and the major changes that this entailed from a structural perspective presented an opportunity to bring about real change in how services were delivered.

The canteen and water-cooler conversations in the early days of our transformation programme were predictable. The majority of staff in the HSE could identify with a vision of providing much better access to care, and a seamless care pathway. However, most people had seen proposals before for major change only to watch the vision slowly fade. Therefore, it would be unfair to criticise people for saying that they had heard it all before and question why this would be different.

One of the biggest obstacles to change in a public sector environment is opposition by the political system and by Government to radical change. This opposition to change is not necessarily the primary response of Government, who often want to see significant change, but are fearful of the political consequences. Professional representative organisations, trade unions and local communities fearful of changes in their local hospital can exert huge influence on politicians and governments, often delaying proposed changes in services. This broadly based fear of change in healthcare is not unique to Ireland. Across the world, change programmes in healthcare have struggled to succeed. International studies have shown that healthcare services are the most resistant of all systems to change.

In such an environment, it was essential that the credibility of the change programme was established early on. If this did not happen, the formal transformation programme had very little chance of success. When I say 'credibility' in this context I refer to the need for us to quickly address some issues that had been contentious for several years and show that we were able to bring about the required changes.

We therefore focused on creating a number of levers that would help to promote change. The book outlines the development of such levers and some of the fundamental changes that had to be achieved if the transformation programme was to have credibility. These included:

- Developing Clinical Leaders (see Chapters 10 and 11)
  A patient-centred model of integrated care with seamless access to most services could only be put in place by clinical leaders. If clinicians were proposing changes such as the development of a team-based approach to providing care or the reconfiguration of hospital services, the public and other health professionals were more likely to accept the changes and therefore the political system was more likely to accept change. A clinical leadership structure had to be developed which allowed clinical leaders to initiate and drive change in the way they and their colleagues provided services.

- Performance Measurement and Management (see Chapter 13)
  This is a fundamental lever in implementing change in a healthcare service. A new, publicly accessible, transparent performance measurement system was required. Using performance measures, clinical leaders can demonstrate to their colleagues and the public why change has to occur if services are to be improved.
- Multidisciplinary Primary Care Teams (see Chapter 9)
  An integrated care system could only be achieved if there were multidisciplinary healthcare teams providing services in the community. This, in itself, was a major change programme, affecting the way most professionals did their work every day. If we could establish the concept of primary care teams early on and get all service providers to move from the professional silos in which they operated into multidisciplinary teams, the transformation programme would garner huge credibility. Those who worked in the health service would begin to accept that this was a real change rather than a cosmetic makeover.
- Hospital Reconfiguration (see Chapters 6–8)
  There had been no reconfiguration of Irish hospitals over the previous thirty years. Initiating such a reconfiguration would provide an important impetus for the change programme. We had to suspend the plan to build 3,000 more hospital beds, as otherwise nobody was going to accept our focus on improving efficiency or our plan to shift investment towards building up community-based services. At the same time, hospitals had to change what they did, focusing on providing services that they were equipped to do safely. Hospitals also needed to provide immediate access for patients to senior decision makers, therefore avoiding the need for hospital admission, if at all possible.
- Unified Management Structure (see Chapter 14)
  Management structures needed to be changed to support the delivery of integrated care. While hospital and community services continued to operate as separate businesses seamless access to care was never going to happen. All services would in future have to operate under a single management structure, with the clinical leadership having the power to redirect funds from one part of the service to another as required. This might seem straightforward, but, in essence, meant merging two very separate structures, each with over 50,000 employees.

- Improved Value for Money (see Chapter 12)
  The HSE would have to achieve much better value for taxpayers' investment if the transformed health services were to be sustainable.

Healthcare organisations in several countries are now focused on developing integrated healthcare systems. Ireland is further along the road than most in developing such a system, having confronted many of the difficult challenges presented in changing how we do things. The foundations have been put in place by thousands of people working in the HSE. There has been an acceptance that building more hospitals and hospital beds is not the solution. There is an acceptance that we need to provide as many of the services as possible through primary care teams working in the local communities, including many services that were previously only available in hospitals. There are now wonderful examples of comprehensive primary care teams that are up and running and are hugely relevant in every respect to the communities they serve (see Chapter 9). There is a lot more to be done to fully develop these services across all areas of the country.

There is also now an acceptance that our hospital services have to be reconfigured and, for the first time in almost fifty years, a significant change in the structure of the hospital system outside Dublin is well underway (see Chapter 7). Within individual hospitals, professionals are now beginning to work in new ways. An excellent example is the development of medical assessment units which allow patients referred from general practitioners (GPs) to be assessed immediately by a senior physician and get rapid access on the same day to diagnostic services like CT scans without the need, as in the past, to be admitted to hospital to access these services. The creation of centres of excellence for cancer care, which is continuing, is another example of this change.

There are now several community intervention teams in place, comprising nurses and other carers who will support an acutely ill person in their own home rather than having to admit that person to hospital. Again, this programme needs to continue and to be expanded across the country.

The Irish healthcare system now has more transparency in terms of performance than most other healthcare systems, with extensive performance measures for hospital and community services available on the HSE's website (www.hse.ie/eng/staff/HealthStat; see Chapter 13).

A major goal of the transformation programme was to make the services much safer for people, but, for some, this did not happen quickly enough. Establishing a new system that puts clinical leaders in positions of authority, reconfigures hospital services so that they are structured in such a way that they are safer, and provides transparency in relation to performance ultimately results in a marked improvement in the quality and safety of services. Everybody had to remain focused on achieving these and other changes, while at the same time responding to the individual incidents that inflicted terrible harm on people we were supposed to be serving. It is difficult to maintain a focus on a change programme like this when the public are understandably extremely upset with the entire organisation because of a case where cancer was misdiagnosed or a child was abused. The reality is that change occurs very slowly, especially in healthcare systems, and it is very difficult for the public and even the staff of the HSE to believe that change is actually happening in the midst of tragedies like this. However, if tragedies derail the transformation programme, such awful events are much more likely to recur in the future.

Professionals working in healthcare may be offended by the suggestion that the system was designed to make things easier for us as providers, rather than optimising the quality of service the patient or client receives. Such offence is understandable at first, but I would ask you to read the story of Tom as outlined in Chapter 1 and then revisit the discussion. Is the story an accurate portrayal of how people have been treated in the past? If it is, can anybody defend the way in which the health service has been structured traditionally or oppose the transformation programme? Can anybody say that the healthcare system that provides Tom's care was designed to provide the best possible service for him? By demonstrating that the healthcare service was structured in a way that could never provide the best possible care for people, hopefully this book may convince those who use the healthcare services that what was acceptable historically should no longer be acceptable.

Reading this, the public may come to see that they have unwittingly played a role in allowing this system to develop. They have done this by failing to ask for, or demand directly from us, the frontline professionals, accountability for providing a proper coordinated service. The reader, I hope, will identify with this because healthcare can only operate at the highest possible level if the public demand a quality service in return for their investment as taxpayers, and if clinicians are focused on their responsibility to provide the leadership required to deliver this type of service.

These two issues are interlinked. Unfortunately, in the past, the public have valued highly the opinion of clinicians who criticised the system and demanded more investment rather than a change in professional practices as a solution to the problems. The public need to begin to demand that we, as healthcare professionals, change how we do things to make access to services much easier and movement from one part of the service to another as seamless as possible. Our new clinical leaders will then feel empowered in continuing to lead the changes in professional practice that are required.

People will hopefully become more aware of the importance of governance in healthcare, just as it is in areas like banking (see Chapter 16). Weak governance in healthcare has not just been a problem for health boards in the past, the HSE, the Government and the Department of Health, but it is equally a challenge in voluntary agencies such as voluntary hospital boards and community-based organisations. It is vital that everybody involved in healthcare governance understands that their primary responsibility is to the public and not to an individual institution, the Department of Health, the Minister or the Government.

This book will really have made a difference if the public begin to take a more proactive approach to determining how health services are organised and demand a continuing focus on the delivery of an integrated healthcare system (Chapter 1). This will only begin to happen when Irish people identify themselves as the funders of the health service and align themselves with assertions like the following:

- I am entitled to a multidisciplinary primary care team in my locality.
- I am entitled to have immediate access to a consultant at a medical assessment unit on the day my GP decides I need an urgent assessment, rather than being admitted to hospital to wait to be seen by the same consultant.
- I require that my elderly parent, who has a number of chronic diseases, has a key worker in the community primary care team who will be their voice in interacting with all parts of the health and social care system.

- I am entitled to an efficient system of care that allows me to return home from hospital with my newborn child within twenty-four hours of delivery, or ensures that my father has his cataract surgery carried out as a day patient, rather than being admitted to hospital.
- I require a community intervention team to be available in my area to treat my elderly mother's chest infection at home with intravenous antibiotics, rather than admitting her to hospital, where she may become confused after a few days and potentially never return home.
- I want ongoing access to performance information in relation to the quality and efficiency of my local health service.
- I insist that my health services are managed by a single management structure across hospital and community and that those who govern the structure are entirely focused on the needs of service users, and not on the requirements of institutions, political systems or service providers.

As a result of the HSE's transformation programme, a lot these things are happening or are already available in different parts of the country. All of these changes need to happen everywhere, but it does require a significant commitment by all the professional groups working in healthcare to change the way we do things. Ultimately, you, the public, get the service you demand. You will not get it if you fail to challenge poor performance. Blaming the ubiquitous system or some unknown or possibly non-existent bureaucrat will not achieve this. The demands outlined above should be seen as a human right. If the public focuses on these demands healthcare professionals will increasingly take on leadership roles in implementing the many changes that are already underway, because such changes are essential if clinicians are to be able to provide this type of seamless care.

CHAPTER 1

Why Integrated Healthcare?

You have been under pressure at work recently and decide to take a short break. On arrival at your hotel, you register at the reception desk. The following morning, you go for breakfast, but the dining-room staff are unable to serve you breakfast because they were unaware that you are staying at the hotel, and, in any event, have already served breakfast to 130 people, which is their daily limit. You have to go through another registration process to try to book breakfast for the following day, but there is no space free for the next two weeks.

After breakfast at a local coffee shop, you decide to use the hotel's pool and gymnasium. Instead of simply providing your room number and name, you have to register again. You are informed that there is no lifeguard between 12.00 p.m. and 2.00 p.m. and therefore you cannot swim at this time.

You return to your room and discover that it hasn't been made up. You call reception but the reception staff cannot deal with your complaint because it is not their department. You must deal directly with the housekeeping department. Housekeeping informs you that you would have needed to register with them a month earlier to arrange a time to have your room cleaned.

You ask to speak to the hotel manager, who understands your frustration but explains that each of the units within the hotel are autonomous and decide when and how they provide services. She, therefore, cannot resolve your problem.

It is obvious how frustrating this organisational structure would be for a hotel's customers. It is also clear how difficult it would be for the hotel to ensure consistency in the quality of its services. This structure leads to a disjointed service, reduces customer satisfaction and damages the hotel's reputation. It is frustrating for those staff who are providing a superb service in their specific area that the hotel's reputation is being undermined by poor performance in other areas over which they have little or no influence.

This structure does, however, have benefits for staff. Housekeeping staff can plan a month in advance how many rooms they will make up and clean in a morning. Similarly, the dining-room staff control their workload and do not have to respond in a flexible way to the challenge created if the hotel reception accepts reservations for extra customers.

If the hotel industry was a monopoly, with no competition, this inflexible structure could easily exist. However, the hotel business is highly competitive and so this is not the case. In fact, staff must strive to cope with all customer demands, even those that are unreasonable. Services are provided in a coordinated manner and the hotel manager is singularly responsible for ensuring that all services, from the car park to the accommodation, from the food to the spa, are provided to the highest possible standard. More importantly, the staff at the hotel ensure that any difficulty that may exist between them in terms of coordinating the provision of services across different areas of the hotel will never be visible to you. Services will continue to be provided in the most seamless way possible, irrespective of any such difficulties. Peer pressure promotes service excellence, as underperformance by any one link in the chain significantly undermines the overall experience of the customer, who rightly identifies the service as a single entity and will not return if the service is poor or inadequate.

Now, let us consider how we deliver health services.

Tom is a 63-year-old man who lives in a town in the west of Ireland. He is an alcoholic, suffers from depression and is separated from his wife. He developed diabetes about ten years ago and had to have his left leg amputated as a complication of his diabetes. More recently, his eyesight has deteriorated significantly. He lives alone in social housing and has little contact with his family.

He has access to a comprehensive array of publicly funded medical and social services in his home town. His general practitioner (GP) provides him with immediate access to care when required. The public health nurse visits him regularly at home and helps him to manage his insulin, although compromises have had to be made because of Tom's lifestyle, such as the number of times he uses insulin each day. She and his GP know that twice daily insulin injections would give him better control of his diabetes. However, from a practical point of view, a once daily injection is more successful, as he is more compliant in the morning and can be supervised for his injection most mornings. Since his amputation, he attends the community physiotherapy clinic and has also had excellent occupational therapy support to assist him in maintaining an independent lifestyle. His deteriorating vision is also the subject of ongoing treatment by the community ophthalmic services. He regularly attends the local mental health clinic, where he is seen by the community psychiatrist or by the community mental health nurse. In addition, he visits an addiction counsellor intermittently. The local social worker continues to support him in every way possible, including trying to rebuild his relationship with his family. The community welfare officer helps to ensure that he receives all benefits that are due to him and that he is adequately housed.

This comprehensive array of services provided for Tom by the public health service, and funded by the Irish taxpayer, is unparalleled in many other countries. Why, therefore, is the healthcare system not considered by the public to be one of the best in the world?

There are problems with the way in which Tom is cared for. All of these health professionals are providing him with the best care possible in the circumstances under which they operate. However, they all operate from separate premises, other than the occupational therapist and physiotherapist who share accommodation in the town. There are no team meetings of the professionals involved in his care, and the only person who informs each of the health professionals of what the others are doing is Tom himself, which he can do to some extent when he is sober and not depressed.

The professionals themselves are frustrated by the fact that they have no way of developing a comprehensive management plan for Tom's myriad of problems. They know they could provide him with a much better service if they and their fellow healthcare professionals were organised as a team. Instead, each of them works and reports in a structure that encompasses only their own professional unit: for example, physiotherapists report to the area physiotherapy manager and social workers report to the social work manager. Such a working and reporting structure does not facilitate the needs of patients. It does, however, have benefits for each professional group as it ensures that each profession can control access to their services, rather than the patient having one point of access to all services.

The situation becomes more challenging for Tom when, after he was found collapsed and confused on the street at 10.00 p.m. on a Friday night, he is transferred by ambulance to the general hospital, which is in another town thirty miles away. He is admitted under the care of his medical consultant who has not seen him for over a year because he has failed to attend follow-up appointments at the diabetes outpatient clinic. There has been no contact between the hospital consultant and the GP over this period. The hospital consultant decides that Tom's diabetes is not appropriately managed and his insulin dosage and injection regime is altered. It is decided that he should have injections twice a day. This occurs despite the fact that a twice-a-day regime has previously been tried and failed, and for practical reasons has been readjusted by his GP and the public health nurse, as already mentioned.

Tom is also assessed by a psychiatrist in the general hospital and, following the long process of him recounting his story, further alterations in treatment are made. A social worker from the hospital social work department is asked to determine whether or not his family can be encouraged to take part in his ongoing care.

During this admission, an ultrasound of his abdomen is carried out because Tom's liver function tests are abnormal. It is discovered that he has a large aneurysm or dilatation of the main artery in his abdomen, the aorta. While this is a fortuitous discovery, there is a concern that this could rupture at some time.

Tom has now spent twelve days in his local hospital, and has had numerous assessments and changes in treatment, many of which would not have needed to take place if there was close collaboration between the hospital professionals and the professionals in the community who know Tom well and could have provided significant insights into what was likely to be an optimal care plan, considering the practical constraints of his social circumstances. This is not the fault of the hospital service as there is no single point of contact in the community which could inform the hospital of the myriad of services Tom receives. All of his community care professionals are solo practitioners, and therefore hospital professionals would have to interact individually with each of them. Even if this occurred, it would be unlikely to provide the overall picture which could protect Tom from having to undergo a full reassessment in hospital.

Due to concern about the dilatation of the main artery in his abdomen, a decision is made to refer Tom for an expert surgical opinion to the vascular surgery department at a Dublin hospital, which is 150 miles away. A bed is made available for him in the hospital within a couple of days and he is transferred there by ambulance. Following admission to the hospital in Dublin, Tom is reviewed by the vascular surgeon who decides that the dilation of the aorta is indeed significant and he requires surgery. However, given his medical history of diabetes, depression and the likely lack of any family support when he returns home, the vascular surgeon delays the surgery until several issues are clarified. He requests a consultation from a consultant physician, whereupon a complete reassessment of his diabetes is again undertaken, followed by further proposed changes in treatment. The vascular surgeon also requests that the consultant psychiatrist and the mental health team at the hospital assess Tom with a view to determining his mental health status, his capacity to understand the surgery being proposed and the significant risks associated with it, as well as the risks associated with him not having surgery. In addition, the surgeon requests that the social work department become involved to determine how Tom's post-operative care can be managed in the context of a lack of family involvement. These assessments take seven to ten days to complete, during which time he occupies a bed which he has no desire to occupy. Rather, he is intimidated and frightened by his strange surroundings. Meanwhile, other patients wait for a bed in the emergency department of this Dublin hospital.

It is obvious that the structure in which the professionals operate is very frustrating for Tom, as he must coordinate all his care himself. He is also responsible for constantly repeating details of past medical encounters at every point of contact. This healthcare structure is also highly inefficient from the State's perspective, as significant amounts of money are being invested in a system which requires that work is repeated unnecessarily due to the lack of a team approach by professionals treating the same individual. Furthermore, because of this structure Tom is occupying hospital accommodation that he does not want, and which is required for other patients.

If such a service was provided in the hotel industry, it would be considered unacceptable and the venture would fail. However, many healthcare systems across the world operate in the way I have outlined above. Generally, there has been little or no challenge by the public to health services being provided in this way. The provider is allowed to design a system that puts their professional needs first. The user or customer, being dependent for care on the service providers, is in a vulnerable position and therefore does not challenge even the most irrational delivery system.

An Integrated Health Service

Tom's experience illustrates why it was essential for the HSE to initiate its transformation programme to develop an integrated healthcare system for Ireland. Customers of a healthcare system deserve to be treated in a holistic manner by the service; they should not have to seek solutions to each of their problems through different points of contact within the service. A holistic service is also critical to ensuring the quality and safety of treatment. Significant quality and safety risks will always arise when multiple professionals are dealing with problems in an uncoordinated manner.

At meetings with professionals and others soon after taking up the post of CEO of the HSE, I asked the question: if a man from Mars arrived and observed the structures and processes we use to provide care for someone like Tom, how would he react? The answer was obvious to most people. Everyone agreed that Tom's care was being provided in a haphazard manner. Everyone agreed that his care could be provided more effectively and efficiently using a team-based integrated approach.

In an integrated system, all community-based health professionals, including GPs, work as a team and would ideally be located in the same premises. Each complex patient would have a key worker in the team responsible for coordinating his or her care. Similarly, hospitals have to re-organise their work practices to interact in a planned and organised way with the community-based primary care teams, greatly reducing the need for patients to be admitted to hospital, and, when they are, markedly reducing the length of time spent in hospital.

Hospital and community services have to be managed through a single budget, reinforcing the need for cooperation between the services, with a single manager for the integrated service. This can be compared with the hotel manager's responsibility for all facets of the hotel's services, and the potential to move both personnel and financial resources from one area to another to maximise quality.

There is, then, an alternative way to handle Tom's care. He could remain at home until just before his surgery if the professionals managing his care in the community are organised as a multidisciplinary team, with one member of the team appointed as his key worker to liaise with the other team members and with other services such as hospitals. His key worker from the local team provides all the information required by the doctors in the nearby general hospital and by the surgeon in Dublin about the management of Tom's diabetes, as well as his depression, and coordinate a plan to manage his convalescence. He is sent home from his local general hospital and only moves to Dublin when a detailed plan for his surgery and post-operative care is agreed, following a full assessment of his scans by the surgeons in Dublin. His return home for convalescence is also speeded up by ongoing close contact between his community-based team and the hospital.

All of this, to the non-clinical reader, sounds extremely logical and many may ask why this new system was not implemented immediately by the HSE. This assumes that achieving change or transformation in the way we provide care should be relatively simple, and that it could be accomplished in one to two years. Many may ask why these changes are taking so long. The answer is that, while the required changes may be obvious to most individuals who work in the healthcare sector, changing from the way we have worked for years to a new team-based integrated approach is a huge change for healthcare workers. This is not just an Irish problem but occurs in many developed countries. Healthcare providers are comfortable working in professional silos. GPs work as individuals or provide services as a group practice; physiotherapists work together; social workers work together. In hospitals, the majority of consultants operate as individuals rather than in a multidisciplinary team-based service.

As mentioned, working in professional groups or silos ensures that everyone, apart from general practitioners and emergency departments, who are the front offices for the health service, can control access to their services. A patient cannot move seamlessly across compartmentalised professional groups but rather is considered by each group as a new customer who must register with each service provider. Therefore only GPs have to respond immediately to the demand for non-emergency services from the public. In contrast, allowing patients access to all services through a single point of contact (a primary care team) means that professionals have to become more flexible in responding immediately to a patient's needs. As in the hotel industry, all other members of the team quickly become aware of where the strong and weak links exist in the chain in a seamless service. For example, a GP refers a patient to a therapist and the patient is told there is four-month waiting list. The GP has no way of knowing if this is due to the volume of work referred to the therapist or due to inefficiencies in how the service is delivered. In a team environment the answer to this question is usually obvious. All of us would hesitate to move from a system which allows us a large degree of control over our workload, and limits the visibility of the effectiveness of our work practices, to one where we have to respond to a demand immediately and, perhaps more importantly, where our performance is more visible to other members of the team.

Another dimension to this is that when we work in professional silos we tend to reassure each other that failures in the overall service are not our responsibility and, indeed, we often identify other groups as being responsible. The GP is frustrated that the public health nurse is unavailable at weekends or the occupational therapist is frustrated that the consultant is too busy to write the reports required to supply home aids or appliances. Moving to a team-based environment means that if the service is underperforming the team, as a unit, must take responsibility and decide how they are going to improve performance to meet agreed local and national targets.

Integrating community-based services into a team structure is only one part of this transformation; there is also a need to formally link community services and hospital services to provide a seamless transition for patients. Those of us who have spent most of our professional lives working in hospitals can become oblivious to the fact that we also have to change how we practise and care for patients. In an integrated system, planning patient care does not require the patient being physically present in the hospital for several days while the plan is formulated. Admitting patients to hospital is a very convenient way for me as a clinician to provide services. The patient is waiting and available on whatever day or at whatever time suits me. Many patients are in hospital not because they need to be but simply because it is more convenient for various healthcare professionals to see the patient and schedule tests or investigations. It is impossible to imagine any other service where the customer would accept such a service.

The alternative, which would apply in most other services, is that the customer, the patient, would present to the hospital at an appointed time for each assessment or investigation, and the provider would be available at that time to provide the service. New medical assessment units, now opening in hospitals, allow patients referred by their GPs to the local hospital as urgent cases to be seen on the same day by a senior clinician in the hospital without them having to be admitted to the hospital. This is a very different way of working for a hospital consultant. Under these circumstances, patients should not end up wandering corridors in their dressing gowns from morning to evening, waiting to be seen by a doctor or to be called for an investigation. Almost no patient who is well enough to wander the hospital corridor should be required to be in hospital. Consider this the next time you visit a hospital.

Getting Buy-In for Change

While Tom's story helps to explain why an integrated system is so essential if we are to provide the best possible care for those who need it, it also provides some insight into why developing such a system is a major challenge. Transformation is a word that probably turns a lot of people off. Clinicians view such a term as code for bureaucrats wanting to be seen to be doing something while never intending to deliver anything of substance. The HSE's challenge from 2005 to 2010 was to paint a picture of change that would improve services for patients and show that the change was not only logical but achievable, if everybody committed to it.

In initiating the transformation programme, focused on building an integrated system of care, we appealed to the altruism of healthcare professionals to bring about the changes required. We asked people to consider how they would like to be treated themselves if they were in Tom's situation. A significant number of people realised that this was not how they would like to be treated, nor would they want their parents or relatives to be so treated. Identifying how unreasonable the processes in our health service were resulted in people beginning to accept that change was needed and that the changes were not necessarily complex. In fact, removing complexity and simplifying the way we provided services was the target of the transformation programme, creating an integrated system of care.

CHAPTER 2

Management of the Health Service up to 2005

Up until 2005 the Department of Health and Children was responsible to the Government for the provision of all health and personal social services and was accountable for delivering these services within the voted allocation of funds each year. The Department disbursed the health and personal social services budget, and delegated responsibility for the delivery of services to thousands of agencies. These included area health boards, large voluntary hospitals, voluntary providers of community services such as disability services and mental health services, and thousands of smaller agencies such as wheelchair associations, rape crisis centres and many more.

Health boards had been established under the Health Act of 1970 to take responsibility for the provision of all services directly provided by the State (as against those provided through voluntary bodies). This included State-owned hospitals and community facilities. The health boards were also responsible for coordinating the provision of State-funded general practice (GP) services. Subsequently, the health boards were given the remit of managing the State's engagement with community-based voluntary agencies in areas such as disability, childcare and some mental health services. Voluntary hospitals did not come under the remit of the health boards and continued to interact with and report directly to the Department of Health and Children.

There were eight area health boards. Because of the predominance of voluntary hospitals in Dublin, with almost no State-owned hospital services, the Eastern Health Board, which covered the Dublin area, was to a large extent focused on community services. Even then, voluntary providers played a significant role in the provision of such services. In 1999, the Eastern Regional Health Authority was established to take responsibility for commissioning all services in the eastern region, including those provided by voluntary agencies. The plan was that the voluntary agencies that provided the majority of services in the Dublin region would now interact directly with the Eastern Regional Health Authority rather than with the Department of Health and Children. Three area health boards were established in the old Eastern Health Board area to manage services not under the control of voluntary agencies.

Each year, individual health boards developed a service plan, agreed with the Department, which outlined the services to be provided during that year. The main measurable elements in the service plans were measures of activity, for example the number of outpatients, inpatients or procedures that were provided during the year. Generating more activity was seen as an indicator of success.

The delivery of health services was subject to direct political control at all levels. The Department of Health and Children reported to the Minister. At the next level, health boards were largely composed of local political representatives with occasional healthcare professionals, but there was no formal consumer representation and no independent professional input from outside the local area.

The requirement for agreement between these stakeholders, i.e. the Department of Health and Children, health boards and politicians, ultimately determined the quality of health service provided rather than the objective of providing the best possible care based on the funds invested. Two critical interdependencies were the health boards' dependence on the Department and the Department's dependence on the political system.

The health boards obtained almost all of their funding through the Department. Each health board saw itself in competition with the other health boards in obtaining funds from the Department. This placed the Department in an extremely powerful position. Visits by Department officials to health board areas were of major importance. This empowerment of officials was in itself a disincentive to the Department to do anything to alter the competitive health board structure.

The Department's dual role of having responsibility for service provision and being accountable to the Government for adherence to health policy diminished the chance of providing optimal services in return for the investment provided by taxpayers. In Ireland, health ministers are members of parliament and must be responsive to their own backbenchers. The Irish healthcare system was therefore, in effect, directly managed by the political system. Local county councillors who were members of health boards could object to any proposed changes in services that affected their local area by lobbying their local TD, who could then apply pressure on the Minister for Health who in turn had direct control over the Secretary General of the Department of Health and Children and his or her officials. Therefore, there was a complete circle of political control affecting all points of service planning and delivery, which ultimately determined what changes were implemented.

As a result of this, everybody identified that change, even when such change was in the interest of patients, could be frustrated by politics. The major stakeholders in the provision of healthcare, including healthcare professionals, were aware of this remarkable feedback loop within the health and political system and came to use it to their own advantage, as did every interest group. This varied from a local hospital action group objecting to reconfiguration and rationalisation plans to make hospital services safer to major voluntary agencies in hospitals, or community services lobbying successfully to protect their agencies' interests whenever changes that could affect their independence or survival were proposed.

Changing a healthcare delivery system that had such a close alignment with the political system was almost impossible. The political system was happy because it exerted control, which is what determines its relevance. The only group in the political system who may not have been happy were members of the Cabinet, because underperformance of services could threaten the continued existence of their government. The Department was happy with such a structure because it maintained its control over the delivery system and ensured that the provision of services was not altered by health board executives in ways that resulted in dissatisfaction among its political masters.

Professionals, including nurses, doctors, therapists, social workers and many others who provided frontline services, were also beneficiaries of a politically controlled health service. This may seem surprising because these were the individuals who often complained about political interference and control of the system. However, political control of the system allowed trade unions and professional representative bodies to exert influence over any changes that were proposed.

A politically controlled system was never going to be subject to adequate performance management. It was not in the interest of a health board or local political representatives to expose underperformance in their area because underperformance is often the result of the way services are configured. Raising concerns about the performance of services might have led to services being moved or provided in a new or different way that would not be consistent with local political requirements. Inefficiency was protected in such an environment. There were many examples of this across Ireland, such as hospital surgical or emergency departments that were (and some still are) staffed twenty-four hours a day with little activity after 9.00 p.m. at night, but which generated considerable overtime bills to cover these periods of very low activity.

It was also not in the interest of most to develop national performance parameters, because to do so might have exposed significant inequity in resource distribution. When we did start to measure performance in the HSE there was marked variability in performance between various parts of the country.

A fundamental flaw in a health service controlled at a political level is that there is seldom any reward for improving performance. Resources are often provided on the basis of waiting lists and public outcry about individual incidents. A high-performing service without long waiting lists, providing a safe, quality service that minimised the risk of major incidents occurring, found it difficult to compete for funding with poorly managed health boards or agencies with large waiting lists. In such a system high performers may have felt the need to generate problems to justify more resources.

Direct political control of the healthcare system also undermined managers. The senior management of the health boards were regularly accused of administering the service rather than managing it. This was a self-fulfilling prophecy in systems that were essentially under direct political control. Even the most committed manager, who focused on optimising services from a patient's perspective, rapidly became frustrated when his or her decisions were undermined by the political imperative to maintain the status quo in terms of the configuration of services in an area. Such individuals could become disillusioned once they discovered that managing effectively was likely to result in damage to their career prospects. They often started out being very committed to improving public service, but became administrators as this was all that they could hope to do in such a system.

There are many examples of the practical effects this had on patient services. In one health board, a CEO fought a brave battle against the political system over a number of years on the need to amalgamate hospital services onto a smaller number of sites. His proposals, however, were rejected. Subsequently, a number of major incidents, including cancer misdiagnosis, occurred at some of the hospital sites that he had tried to reorganise. Even when the need for reconfiguration became obvious, his name was never mentioned in the context of what he had tried to achieve.

Other health boards made decisions to divide cancer services for small populations across two or three hospital sites. These decisions were based on the need to get an even distribution of the new service across all hospital sites, rather than the achievement of the best possible services for patients. It was clear to all involved that there was no clinical justification for some of the decisions and that, in fact, optimal patient care was undermined by such decisions. Despite this, these decisions were implemented. A few years later, there were major problems with cancer misdiagnosis in one of the areas in question.

Executives often felt that they had to agree to such a configuration of services as they wished to be seen as astute, understanding the political imperative to reach agreement with all stakeholders and having the capacity to ensure that consensus was achieved. Any executive who wished to be appointed by the Government to important national boards would have to adopt such an approach, as it confirmed that they could be depended upon not to undermine the political system in any way, such as pointing out to the public that patients were being put at risk by political decisions. In contrast, healthcare managers who advocated for services to be based on what was best for patients were unlikely to be appointed to such national boards in a system that was politically controlled.

It became obvious that day-to-day political control of the Irish health service was counterproductive. We had almost fifty hospitals providing services to a population of four million people. Attempts at reconfiguration had failed. This organisation of services was unsafe from a patient's perspective, with activity levels in areas like intensive care and cardiac care extremely low in many hospitals. A number of hospitals only had two to three patients each month placed on a ventilator (indicating severe illness) and yet continued to run intensive care and coronary care units. Acute surgical services continued in many of these hospitals, despite the fact that overnight surgery practically never occurred on some sites, and the overall volume of surgery outside of minor procedures was miniscule. The public were unaware of the low levels of activity as such figures were never provided. In fact, the vast majority of people in Ireland believed that all hospitals were extremely busy places and that all professionals who worked in healthcare were significantly overworked.

In this politically controlled system, there was also a failure to challenge major suppliers of healthcare equipment and contractors for healthcare facilities. Each health board did most of its own procurement. The extra cost to the taxpayer of obtaining supplies and services in this way was very significant. Similarly, there was no national estates function for construction or remodelling of infrastructure, and the provider of services again had all the advantages in negotiating contracts with relatively small healthcare provider agencies. Such agencies could not justify employing professional architectural and engineering experts in negotiating contracts. Maintaining local control over contracts in areas like procurement and estates was seen as beneficial by the politically controlled health board. Following the establishment of the HSE, highly effective national estates and procurement departments were established leading to significant savings being achieved in expenditure on supplies and services ranging from telephone communications to legal services, and to major new building developments.

Large voluntary agencies, which provided taxpayer-funded services, were rarely challenged in a politically controlled environment. Dublin, for example, continued to maintain three children's hospitals, providing a mixture of general and highly specialised tertiary services on all sites at a time when cities like Birmingham and Toronto, with populations of four to five million, had all of their tertiary services on one site. The increased risk for children associated with providing complex services across three sites was known, but no attempt was made to amalgamate the hospitals.

Similarly, in the adult hospitals, cancer services were provided on five sites in Dublin because there were five major hospitals. There was no other justification for maintaining comprehensive cancer services across five sites.

The HSE, following its establishment, initiated a national programme for the reconfiguration of hospitals and their services. While such changes are never popular, the effect of this reconfiguration programme has already resulted in significant changes and the ongoing changes over the next five years will be huge in terms of their capacity to make services safer and more cost effective. Such change had not been achieved in the twenty years prior to the setting up of the HSE, and probably never could be initiated in a system under direct political control.

CHAPTER 3

The Decision to Establish the Health Service Executive

The HSE was established in 2005, with a Board appointed by the Minister for Health and Children, to take responsibility for the delivery of all health and personal social services in Ireland. It was responsible for these services whether they were provided directly through government-owned facilities or through agreements with voluntary organisations, such as the major Dublin hospitals. The HSE was to operate by agreeing a service plan each year with the Government, outlining the services it would deliver based on the budget provided to it. The Department would withdraw from day-to-day provision of services and would in essence be responsible for guiding the Government in the development of healthcare policy. It would also be responsible for monitoring the HSE in fulfilling its role in delivering services.

The setting up of the HSE contains potentially important lessons for health services internationally. Its establishment can be seen as a determined and courageous effort by the Government to distance the management of the health service on a day-to-day basis from political and other interference, and therefore to allow it to focus on achieving a high quality and safe service for patients.

The decision to establish the HSE followed a number of very comprehensive reports which had identified significant problems in the governance and effectiveness of the Irish health service. A health strategy for Ireland, entitled *Quality and Fairness – A Health System for You*, was published by the Department of Health and Children in 2001, and was followed by several other reports focusing on how the strategy could be achieved. In 2003, an audit of structures and functions in the health service (referred to as the Prospectus Report) proposed the setting up of the HSE. Separately, the Brennan Commission made 136 recommendations related to improving the performance of the healthcare system, with a particular focus on quality and value for money.

Both the Brennan and Prospectus Reports carried out remarkably detailed assessments of the Irish healthcare system, following which each of them provided robust backing for a national agency to be established, with a remit to focus on improving the quality and efficiency of the health service.

Other reports focused on particular aspects of the health service. As part of the overall health strategy, an excellent primary care strategy, *Primary Care: A New Direction*, was published in 2001 by the Department of Health and Children. However, by 2005, four years later, only ten primary care teams had been established, and the strategy appeared to have stalled. In 2003, the *Report of the National Task Force on Medical Staffing* – the Hanly Report – courageously proposed a total reconfiguration of Irish hospital services, to ensure safer, high quality services, and better training for clinicians. There was an immediate public outcry against the Hanly Report proposals, and no such reconfiguration of hospitals was advanced prior to the establishment of the HSE.

Towards the end of the planning phase for the HSE, a new Minister for Health and Children, Ms Mary Harney, was appointed to replace Mr Micheál Martin, who had agreed to the establishment of the HSE. Despite this change in political leadership, the commitment to the establishment of the new organisation remained firm.

It is important to try to identify what the key stakeholders saw as the likely role of the HSE following its establishment. Both Mícheál Martin and Mary Harney seemed determined to create a distance between the political system and the day-to-day management of health services. However, the wider political spectrum, including backbench TDs and the local political system, were concerned that they were losing control over the planning and management of health services at a local level. They lobbied the Government to maintain local health boards or authorities that would continue to exert control over the planning and delivery of services. The Government held a firm line in refusing to appoint regional politically based health boards.

The Department and its officials saw the HSE as an agency that would take on much of the operational work that they had to deal with. They would now be able to involve themselves in the less demanding area of developing policy and simply play a policing role in terms of confirming the delivery of services by the HSE. They believed, at that stage, that the HSE would respond to the political system and to the Department in the same way as health boards had done previously, because the Department would remain the budget holder for the health service.

Major voluntary agencies, which owned hospitals and other healthcare facilities, at first did not feel impacted by the development of the HSE. They believed the HSE was not going to affect their long-established direct access to officials in the Department and the political system.

Major contractors such as GPs and pharmacists, as well as representative groups for nurses and hospital doctors, did not oppose the establishment of the organisation. They did not see the creation of the HSE as impacting to any degree on their capacity to influence developments in healthcare that affected their individual groups. They saw it as an administrative change only.

The perception of most stakeholders was that the HSE would take full responsibility for delivering all services within budget. The establishment of the HSE would remove interference by local politicians in health service decisions. The political interface for the health services would be between the Department of Health and Children and national politicians. The point of political influence was essentially being moved from local health boards to TDs operating through the Minister and the Department of Health and Children. The HSE would have no role in policy-making, and it was expected by most that it would do as requested by the Department of Health and Children. The HSE would also take the blame for any failures in the system, allowing the Department to be distanced from such occurrences.

Many of these perceptions were altered due to a remarkable decision made by Minister Mary Harney soon after her appointment. She made a decision to make the CEO of the HSE the accounting officer responsible for the entire budget or vote, as it is known by the Government, allocated to the HSE annually. Up until this time, almost all major government budgets were controlled by the secretary general of the department responsible for the particular area of expenditure. Control over the voted budget is clearly very important in determining the independence of any organisation in pursuing its business agenda. The Minister's decision that the HSE would have full responsibility for its own vote, vested in the CEO, brought with it huge responsibilities for the organisation and the CEO in terms of financial probity, but also gave much greater power to the organisation in terms of its stakeholder interactions and ultimately its credibility in driving a major change agenda.

Transferring control of the budget to the HSE created a very necessary change in the dynamic that developed between the HSE at a corporate level and its own hospitals and other service units. It also led to a major change in the dynamic between the HSE and the large voluntary agencies involved in healthcare provision in Ireland. Attempts by any agency to use the political system to circumvent decisions by the HSE in relation to the optimal use of resources were, as a result, significantly undermined, as those resources were now placed directly in the control of the HSE for use according to an agreed service plan with the Government. The service plan is a public document and has to be adhered to. There was therefore little room left for backroom political deals in relation to the use of resources. It was a momentous decision by the Minister, which reduced the influence the political system had over everyday healthcare services. This did not mean that the Minister was removing the political system from involvement in healthcare, as the service plan was agreed each year with the HSE and was based on government policy in relation to the delivery of health services.

The decision to transfer responsibility for the vote to the HSE also had an effect on how senior civil servants in the Department viewed the HSE and its impact on them. It suddenly became apparent that the HSE was being empowered to plan and deliver services in a manner that the Department themselves had never been allowed to do. This created a risk that the public and health service staff would identify a significant difference between the way services were planned and implemented under the HSE compared to what happened under the Department of Health and Children. For example, when the HSE immediately began to question the contractual arrangements that existed with various providers, such as the pharmaceutical industry, dentists, doctors and others, the question immediately arose as to why contractual relationships that were extremely beneficial to the suppliers of services had been put in place and left in place for so long. Similarly, the HSE adopting a proactive approach to the reconfiguration of hospital services across the country and in relation to reconfiguring specialist services, such as cancer services and the children's hospitals, raised questions as to why these changes had not happened over the previous twenty years.

Concern existed within the Department of Finance and the Department of Health and Children that the HSE and its CEO could not be relied on as the vote holder to control expenditure. This proved to be wrong. While the health services over the previous thirty years had regularly overspent their allocated annual budget, the HSE between 2005 and 2010 always controlled expenditure within its voted budget.

To be fair, it is understandable that the Department of Health and Children was concerned about an organisation not directly under political influence determining how services were provided to the public, while at the same time it remained under political pressure to limit changes in the healthcare system that affected politicians at a local level. Furthermore, the Department was aware that it was going to be subjected to significant pressure from the political system if decisions taken by the HSE affected powerful stakeholders in industry or professional groups.

In this context, the Department had to try to develop significant defences against the HSE implementing changes that upset the political system. Its own reason for existence was going to be questioned by the political system if it could not be seen to exert control. The Department had to try to ensure that, now the HSE was in control of the budget, it did not start doing things that, while sensible from the perspective of improving the quality of service, were politically unacceptable.

The Department had a number of ways in which it could still exert some control. The appointment of the Board was within the Minister's remit and therefore Department officials were always going to have the capacity to influence some board members. Second, most of the management of the HSE were appointed from within the old health board structure and health board executives traditionally saw themselves as ultimately being under the control of the Department on which they depended for funding. It was important for the Department that this perception did not change in the context of the creation of the HSE. Thus, exerting influence over those below the senior management team within the HSE was always going to be a potential control lever.

It is remarkable that so many senior managers in the HSE chose to ignore these attempts to control them and committed fully to implementing the transformation programme. Huge changes, such as the reconfiguration of hospitals in the North East, Mid-West and South, the savings achieved in reducing the cost of drugs, and the redirection of resources and focus from building thousands of more hospital beds to developing primary care teams, which had not been achieved in the previous thirty years under a civil service controlled system, were set in motion because of that commitment.

Political and civil service systems will, by their nature, avoid making difficult decisions, if at all possible. The HSE was going to be of no relevance if it was not willing to make such decisions. In this context, it should have come as a surprise to no one within the HSE that the organisation was constantly facing a battle in seeking public support. Issues such as changing the configuration of hospitals and other services, challenging staff with clear measures of their performance, and insisting on better value for money from long-term lucrative contractual arrangements were never going to be popular. The different groups affected by each change may have very little in common, but can collectively become a very powerful alliance in the face of a programme of genuine rather than cosmetic change.

It may seem paradoxical, but an unwavering commitment to serving the public interest is generally going to make an organisation unpopular. Understanding and accepting this, if we are genuine in our demand for efficient, effective public services, is probably one of the most critical challenges in present-day Ireland.

Chapter 4

Establishing the New Organisation

Amalgamation

Bringing about the amalgamation of over 20 organisations (other health-related agencies in addition to the health boards were included), several of them with over 5,000 employees, was always going to be an enormous undertaking. Considering that this was a public service environment, planning for such a change would normally have taken place over several years and the actual amalgamation would have taken many years more. However, in the case of the HSE, the Government was proactive and determined that the organisation should be established quickly. An interim board was established in 2004 and this evolved on 1 January 2005 into the actual board of the HSE under the executive chairmanship of Mr Kevin Kelly. During the first six months of 2005, a transition period existed during which the old health board CEOs remained in place, with a full handover of responsibility completed by 1 July 2005.

The haste with which this amalgamation took place was criticised in subsequent years by many who believed the organisation would have performed more effectively from day one if a prolonged period of planning and change management had taken place beforehand. It would obviously have made my job easier if more time had been taken, but I have sympathy with the decision by the Government to move rapidly. A slow transition to a new structure would have presented opportunities for any interest groups that felt threatened by the new structure to undermine the process. Nevertheless, there is no denying that, from the time of its establishment, the organisation faced significant risks related to the rapidity with which all of the old structures were disbanded and the new organisation established.

Kevin Kelly was a highly respected Irish businessman who had managed large banking and insurance companies. The job he was asked to undertake in amalgamating the existing health boards and many smaller agencies, involving approximately 100,000 people, was immense. There is no doubt that his business acumen and experience was always going to be important in undertaking this task. However, a major Achilles heel for this entire process was the limited amount of input from clinicians. Clinicians, including nurses, doctors, physiotherapists, psychologists and professionals in social care, accounted for approximately 70,000 of the workforce. The transition team established under Kevin Kelly largely consisted of executives from the existing health boards or voluntary hospitals with expertise in human resources, finance and operations. As a result, the process was identified by healthcare professionals as an amalgamation of bureaucratic structures, rather than the formation of a single healthcare authority focussed on improved delivery of clinical services. It is likely that the majority of healthcare professionals in 2004 were oblivious to any of the changes taking place, even though it was to have immense personal and professional significance for many of them.

The original Board of the HSE had only two clinicians, one nurse and one doctor, among its eleven members. The rest of the Board was composed of individuals mainly from legal, banking and academic backgrounds.

The fundamental structure of the HSE was based on two service delivery pillars or business units. The first pillar was the National Hospitals Office, which would manage and control all of the country's hospitals. All other services were allocated to the second pillar, referred to as Primary Community and Continuing Care (PCCC). This included primary care services provided by GPs as well as community-based services ranging from public health nursing to physiotherapy and occupational therapy. In addition, the PCCC pillar was also to take full responsibility for mental health, disability, childcare and protection, and personal social services.

It was apparent early on that there were significant tensions between the Executive Chairman, Kevin Kelly, and the Department of Health and Children. Kelly, having been given the task of amalgamating the different agencies and forming a single organisation, was moving at a pace he was accustomed to in the private sector. He may have underestimated the capacity of many stakeholders to resist change in a public service environment. Such resistance by various stakeholders in healthcare is nearly always manifested through the political system and, as a result, the Department of Health.

The agreement of the trade unions was essential to bringing about an amalgamation of public service bodies. The critical trade union involved was IMPACT (Irish Municipal Public and Civic Trade Union), which mainly represented management and administrative grades within the existing health authorities and agencies, as well as some of the clinicians such as therapists. The Government saw the creation of the HSE as a means of rationalising the number of managers and administrators in the system and it was obvious to IMPACT that this reorganisation could have a significant effect on their members. They therefore withheld support for the creation of the HSE until they were provided with certain guarantees by the Government. In the last days of December 2004, because of the pressure that the Government was under to succeed in establishing the HSE by January 2005, it agreed to provide critical guarantees to members of IMPACT, which were underpinned by legislation.

Such provisions were entered into the Health Act 2004, which established the HSE, in relation to the rights of all staff moving to the new organisation. Under section 60 of the Act, all employees transferring to the HSE were guaranteed the maintenance of all terms and conditions that they had prior to moving to the HSE, unless the alteration was agreed with the recognised trade unions or associations of employees concerned. So, while the Government was passing legislation around achieving much greater efficiencies in the use of management and administrative staff in the health service, they were also confirming that all health service employees were guaranteed ongoing employment and did not have to move from their existing place of work.

Not surprisingly, this decision by Government, which resembled a *Yes Minister*-type manoeuvre, was to have a marked effect on the capacity of the HSE to deliver on its responsibilities to maximise the effectiveness of the health service. The most important guarantee provided to existing health board employees was that nobody was required to move to a new work location as a result of the creation of the HSE. This had two important consequences for the fledgling HSE. In the first instance, it made it very difficult to centralise staff working in critical corporate functions, who had the required expertise, to ensure that the HSE would work as effectively as possible from the outset. Establishing national offices as quickly as possible in areas like finance, human resources and procurement was vital to the new organisation, but was almost impossible to achieve under such circumstances. Equally important, very capable managers found their responsibilities were moved to corporate headquarters while they remained in old health board offices with little or nothing to do. These individuals understandably felt undervalued and became frustrated. This frustration manifested itself as antagonism towards the new organisation. At a personal level, it is easy to understand how individuals who had committed much of their working lives to the health service felt that they had been cast aside with no acknowledgment of their expertise or of their contribution to Irish healthcare. However, while this happened with several individuals, it is even more important to acknowledge that many staff from the old health boards displayed great flexibility and contributed enormously as senior managers to the establishment of the HSE.

Appointing a CEO

Kevin Kelly and the Board of the HSE proceeded to appoint a CEO for the organisation. They subsequently announced the appointment of Professor Aidan Halligan to the position. Professor Halligan was an Irishman who had worked as a consultant obstetrician in the UK and, prior to his proposed appointment to the HSE, was working in the area of clinical governance with the National Health Service at the UK Department of Health. A contract with Aidan was agreed by the Board and his appointment was publicly announced. However, a number of weeks later, Aidan announced that he was not taking up the position.

The Board of the HSE appointed PricewaterhouseCoopers (PwC) to engage in a search process to identify a new CEO. I was approached around March 2005 by PwC. I had previous national experience in healthcare as chairman of Comhairle na nOspidéal, which was the national authority responsible for planning the appointment of consultants and therefore exerted a major influence on the organisation of hospital and mental health services, especially the development of new clinical services. I had never given any consideration to the post of the CEO of the HSE. In some respects, I suppose this reflected a worrying lack of interest or knowledge in the wider healthcare community about the new organisation. Or perhaps it reflected the lack of significant belief among clinicians that the HSE represented a potential for real change in the approach to the provision of health services.

Following our initial discussions, I read a lot of the reports and plans that lay behind the establishment of the HSE. I realised at an early stage that there was a lack of detail in relation to the potential impact that the HSE might have on the delivery of clinical services to patients. There was much more detail available in the area of developing shared services, reducing administrative and backroom costs, and the numbers employed in these functions. This would ultimately represent a difference between what the Board of the HSE saw as its remit and my wish to use the HSE to change the entire process of healthcare delivery.

So, why did I even consider taking on the role of CEO of the HSE? This is a question I am frequently asked. At the time, I was a busy paediatric gastroenterologist with academic responsibilities, including the leadership of an internationally recognised research programme. However, I always had a great interest in improving services as a whole. Early in my career, I realised that as an individual clinician you could have a great impact on children and individual families you meet, but at the end of the day your overall impact is confined to a relatively limited geographic area and a small number of individuals. One way of having a wider impact was to become involved in teaching and research. Teaching presents perhaps one of the greatest opportunities for clinicians to have a much wider impact because classes of 100–200 students graduating from a medical school each year can have a very significant effect on the way health services are provided to the public.

I saw a huge opportunity for improving the overall health service. My work as chairman of Comhairle na nOspidéal for a five-year period (1995–2000) had given me a broad insight into Irish health services. I had seen my appointment as chairman of Comhairle as an opportunity to drive the reconfiguration of Irish hospital services in a direction that would significantly improve the quality of the services. This task proved impossible for Comhairle to achieve, as every hospital across the country was intent on maintaining its existing services. I viewed the proposed HSE structure as creating an opportunity to bring about this change, and to develop a much more integrated system of care delivery, which was essential if we were to improve care for people in Ireland.

I also believed that, by taking on the role of CEO of the HSE, I could make the building of a new children's hospital a national healthcare priority. For the previous fifteen years, following my return to Ireland after spending almost a decade at the Hospital for Sick Children in Toronto, I was committed to developing a new children's hospital for Ireland. I believed that there was an opportunity to develop a hospital that would be internationally recognised for the quality of its care.

Overall, the HSE appeared to present an opportunity to bring about a real transformation in how we provided health services. I met with the Board to discuss my interest in the post. In early May 2005, I was informed that the Board wished to appoint me as CEO. The salary for the position, including all benefits and bonus payments, had already been agreed with Professor Halligan and I did not seek any alteration in this package. However, difficulties began to arise in relation to two critical areas, from my perspective, before I would agree to take up the post.

The first issue was my requirement to be seconded to the post from my existing appointment as professor of paediatrics, thereby ensuring that I could return to that appointment at any time. This, from my perspective, was essential if I was going to be able to operate with true independence in driving forward a change agenda for the Irish health service. Based on my previous experience at Comhairle na nOspidéal, I knew that the political system and the civil service exerts control in a very subtle but powerful way over individuals in positions of authority who are not conforming with their requirements. I believed that the most powerful control that they could exert over me, as the HSE progressed with a change agenda that would not be popular in political circles, was the threat of my having to leave the post of CEO on their demand. Resisting this pressure, with no alternative option for employment in Ireland, given the specialised nature of my job, would have been difficult.

My concerns were reaffirmed by the resistance that emerged to the idea of my secondment to the HSE. Such resistance was surprising as, across the public sector in Ireland, individuals are regularly seconded to take up other positions for specific terms of office. It would be unrealistic to expect an individual to give up a professional career and move to a five-year post, particularly one with inordinate risks associated with the need to challenge powerful vested interests.

The second issue of concern was my wish to bring with me into the HSE up to six individuals in an advisory capacity. These would be individuals with expertise in areas in which I believed we had to bring about radical change as soon as possible. These areas included:

- Performance measurement and management.
- The development of primary care with more community-based clinical services.
- Strategic communications in relation to the overall change programme.
- Improving operational efficiency.
- Optimising our working relationship with the voluntary sector.

These people would not be encumbered by career expectations and could challenge different interests without fear of the consequences for their career development. I knew that there were going to be many occasions when we would have to challenge interest groups, from representatives of healthcare professionals to political representatives, and that this would not be easy for those who had worked for many years in the health service, and, indeed, would have to remain within the health service management after I had departed.

The Board had significant concern about advisors being appointed. They explained their resistance to this on the basis of the costs associated with such appointments. This was a surprise, since expenditure on healthcare at that time was €11.5 billion annually. I believed that the resistance to appointing expert advisors, who would provide me with the required support to drive forward a change programme, was due to the fact that they would not be subject to the normal controls exerted over permanent employees by the political and civil service system.

In essence, the arguments surrounding my secondment and the appointment of advisors appeared to me to be mainly related to a fear of loss of control by the Department over me, in implementing a change programme, and that this could result in a situation where change might happen, irrespective of opposition by various interests.

Several meetings took place between the Chairman of the Board, the Minister's personal advisor, the Secretary General at the Department of Health and Children and my legal representative to try to iron out these difficulties. These negotiations ultimately broke down and the following morning I held a press conference where I announced that I was withdrawing from the position. I stated that the lack of support for me being seconded and for advisors joining me in implementing the transformation programme indicated to me that the Board of the HSE and the Department of Health and Children were not committed to real change in the health services.

The political system and the Board reacted with fury to this announcement. In retrospect, perhaps I should have been less forthright in stating my belief that there was a lack of commitment to a change programme. However, at that point, I believed I was definitely detaching myself from the process and this was my only opportunity to be clear as to why I had made my decision to withdraw. The political system and the Board responded by claiming that I refused to take the post because they could not agree to my unrealistic request, in their view, for a secondment.

During this entire process, I developed a very significant respect for both Minister Mary Harney and the recently appointed Secretary General at the Department of Health and Children, Mr Michael Scanlan. I had found Michael Scanlan's commitment to change very encouraging, and I firmly believed that he was personally committed to supporting such change, even in the face of the significant resistance we were likely to face. His role as secretary general was ultimately to prove very important in facilitating the change programme.

After a number of days, communication was re-established to see if we could again discuss my possible appointment as CEO. There were a number of meetings involving the Chairman, the Board of the HSE and me. In the end, there was an agreement. The Board of the HSE accepted the secondment proposal and also the requirement to appoint up to six advisors. This was facilitated by the commitment of UCD, through its president, Dr Hugh Brady, the Director of Research, Professor Des Fitzgerald, and the Executive and Board at Our Lady's Children's Hospital, Crumlin, who all agreed to my secondment to the HSE for a five-year term.

This conflict did, as do most conflicts, leave residual scars that would affect relationships in the future. However, I had to recognise that the

Board of the HSE had themselves been through a very difficult period when they had appointed a CEO on two occasions but both of us had subsequently refused their offer. It was extremely important that we moved forward in a positive frame of mind, especially considering the enormity of the challenge that faced everybody in trying to plan and deliver a major change programme in a new organisation that was bringing together 100,000 employees and stakeholders right across the country.

Chapter 5

The Early Days of the HSE

On day one I was faced with leading a new organisation with 100,000 employees and a budget of €11.5 billion with no established office, secretary or other support staff. Nobody had any idea how this organisation was really going to get up and running. This is not a criticism; it was simply the situation that had to be faced.

The location for the organisation's head office had been chosen as Naas in Co. Kildare, about thirty miles from Dublin. This must have been a political decision, as there was no logical explanation to justify the decision. The HSE was a national organisation, which would require regional managers to come to meetings at its head office regularly. The most efficient way for them to do this would have been to travel by train. Naas is not part of the national rail network. Managers from across Ireland would have to make their way to a train station in Dublin and then take a taxi to Naas, presumably arriving in the afternoon. Alternatively, they would have to stay overnight in Dublin before travelling to Naas for an early morning meeting.

I decided that Naas would not operate as the head office. I was informed that this was a government decision and I could not reverse it. However, I did not intend to have senior managers wasting their time travelling for no good reason. More suitable and convenient office space, which was already in use by the HSE, was located in Dublin close to Heuston Station, the main train terminus for the south and west. Two years later, we moved across the road to the historic Dr Steevens's Hospital building, which the

HSE owned and which no longer functioned as a hospital. Many of the offices were small, but they were adequate, and eventually it was possible to bring most of the corporate team together within this building.

The Management Team

One of the most remarkable aspects of the establishment of the HSE, as a new organisation, was that the Board had appointed the management team prior to the appointment of the CEO. My first meeting with the management team took place on 16 August 2005. The management team members must have had significant concerns about a clinician arriving as CEO of an extremely large and complex organisation, which, as yet, had not been established, except at a most rudimentary level. On reflection, the management team must have wondered how long I would last in my five-year term as CEO.

The management team, as individuals, had, I believe, a variety of views as to what the HSE was meant to achieve or what it was ever likely to achieve. There were a number of people who, I have no doubt, believed that the HSE was one large health board, which would work in the same way as the individual health boards, but would bring some standardisation at a national level that was not possible in the old system.

There were others who could identify the potential of the organisation to bring about significant change in how services were provided, but were sceptical of it ever achieving this potential, based on their experiences of trying to bring about change in a public sector environment. Everybody was careful not to adopt radical positions on change at an early stage, as there was an understandable fear of jumping too quickly onto a ship in a dry dock that might never float.

It was my responsibility to convince people that the organisation had to focus from the beginning on implementing major changes in the way we delivered services. Otherwise, we would simply confirm the fact that we were a large health board. We had to set about creating a vision of what an effective Irish health service would look like and how the HSE as an entity could create the health service of the future. It was vital to convince senior managers, not only on the management team, but at other levels in the organisation, that transformation was possible and that it would ultimately have a major impact on the care provided for people up and down the country. It was also important to be totally honest about the scale of the challenge. This is difficult when you have to explain that evidence from across the world indicates that the transformation programme will likely take years to fully deliver, that, like all change, it will be very unpopular and that ultimately nobody will notice when it happens.

The management team itself faced some criticism because of the way it had been established. There was a view in the organisation that a small select group of people had been handpicked to join the interim team set up to progress the planning and establishment of the HSE (see Chapter 4). Some people believed that anybody who had not been part of that interim team was significantly disadvantaged when it came to competing for senior positions in the new organisation. In such a high risk venture as the establishment of the HSE, the Board of the HSE was understandably more likely to appoint those who had an established track record with the interim organisation ahead of those with whom the Board had not worked previously.

The management team and those who reported to them had to come to terms with how an independent organisation should conduct its business and manage its relationship with the Department of Health and Children and the political system. As mentioned, within the old health board structure each health board courted favour with the Department of Health and Children in the hope that it would get more resources than other health boards. In contrast, the new HSE was going to need managers who would be courageous in exerting their independence from the Department in terms of driving forward a HSE change agenda without fear of the political consequences. It was going to be difficult to change the culture and thinking of individuals from a situation where almost all of their major decisions were double checked by the Department to one where they would act as independent managers. This change was critical to establishing our credibility with the HSE administrative staff, the clinical professionals and the public.

Some members of the management team and senior managers across the country seemed confused as to who they were reporting to, and were as inclined to report to the Department as to the HSE. During my first weeks in office, I became aware that a number of my senior management team were regularly reporting directly to the Department without any reference to me, as CEO. More worrying was the fact that the Department appeared to find it totally appropriate that they should make contact directly with the management of the HSE at any level within the organisation as they saw fit. The need for the HSE, and certainly for a CEO, under such circumstances was questionable.

My insistence on bringing advisors with me into the organisation undoubtedly affected my relationship with some of the senior management team. They interpreted this as a lack of faith in their capacity to manage. It, however, became clear to me very quickly that the members of the management team who were confident in their own abilities had the least concern, or no concern at all, about the arrival of advisors. This in some ways confirmed to me the need for external help.

From the outset, I could identify within the organisation numerous individuals in the management ranks who were extremely capable but who were hesitant to make the necessary decisions. There appeared to be a constant concern that making decisions could result in you being undermined from within the organisation itself. I had to convince people that the HSE would always support individuals who were committed to doing the right thing, even when we made mistakes.

During my first two years as CEO, I made significant changes to the senior management team. These were difficult decisions to make and implement. It was unfortunate for everyone, including the members of the management team, that a team had been put in place prior to my arrival. I was restricted in the decisions that could be made in terms of change at the senior management level, but I had to at least try to develop a team who I believed would be fully committed to change and who would have confidence that the HSE had the capacity to drive real change. It is impossible to achieve this by simply gathering together experienced people from an old organisational structure. We had to promote people from within the existing structure who were passionate about change and also try to bring in new people from outside to challenge us all and stimulate new ways of thinking.

Important Early Interactions

The Clinicians

The response of clinicians, from nurses and doctors to therapists and others in the HSE, was always going to be critical to the success of the organisation. The majority of doctors disliked the health boards and were constantly critical of their performance. Ironically, with the arrival of the HSE, many doctors began to speak quite well of the old health board structure. This is normal human behaviour; everybody is happier dealing with what they know.

The leadership of the nursing profession was more positive about the establishment of the HSE. I met, in the first few weeks, with nursing leaders from across the country and found that they could identify readily with the need for change and, indeed, accept that change was good and was possible.

This acceptance that we needed to change was even more marked among the leaders of the Allied Health Professionals, an umbrella group that was formed to coordinate the activities of professionals, including physiotherapists, occupational therapists, speech and language therapists, podiatrists and dieticians. Their commitment to significant change from the first days of the HSE was remarkable. At an individual level, members of the Allied Health Professional Group across the country appeared much more understanding of the need for change than most other professionals. It is difficult for me to explain why this was the case.

The Voluntary Organisations

Approximately one quarter of the HSE's budget was spent on services provided by voluntary sector organisations, which had been in place for many years in areas such as the acute hospital sector, mental health services and disability services. Some of these organisations, like the Dublin teaching hospitals, were extremely large, with annual budgets of over €200 million each. Historically, many of these organisations were funded directly by the Department of Health and Children. They functioned with remarkable independence and were subject to limited accountability, except in terms of the amount of service that they provided. There was very little measurement of their cost effectiveness or, indeed, of the quality of the services that they provided. Some of these organisations had come together to form umbrella groups to increase their leverage with the Department and with the political system.

Initially, these large voluntary sector organisations did not have any clear indication as to how the HSE would function in relation to them.

They probably held the view that they would continue to interact directly with the Department of Health and Children and exercise significant influence through the political system. It is understandable that they reacted in this manner as, based on their experience of previous health service restructurings, there was no evidence to suggest that any serious attempt would be made to increase their accountability for the expenditure of large amounts of public funds.

To be fair to the voluntary organisations, they subsequently established a constructive relationship with the HSE, realising that the organisation was serious about managing the performance of the health service. The fact that the CEO of the HSE was the vote holder, with full responsibility for the budget, was also an incentive for the voluntary agencies and the HSE to work much more closely together. By 2009, after extensive and at times difficult negotiations, agreement was reached with the voluntary organisations on new service level agreements. These agreements provided for much greater accountability by the voluntary agencies in relation to the expenditure of public money.

Politicians

The establishment of the HSE and its transformation programme was probably one of the most significant public service changes that the political system ever dealt with. The Government itself had established the HSE, and clearly wanted to see significant change, but then had to deal with the fallout that was associated with this change, especially at a local political level. Managing these contradictions was never going to be easy and it was important that those of us who were driving change understood that this was a very difficult environment from a political perspective. However, to establish credibility, the HSE, as an organisation, had to progress the change programme irrespective of political fears. If we were seen to respond to political pressure while pursuing the development of an integrated healthcare service the HSE would be undermined. Getting the balance right between our need to establish the credibility of the organisation and maintaining a good working relationship with the political system at a government level was the challenge.

Politicians are consistently portrayed as the major impediment to healthcare transformation. This belief is generally held by those of us who work in the healthcare services, both managers and healthcare professionals. This would also have been my own impression on taking up the position of CEO at the HSE. I was, however, to discover over the subsequent years that politicians were often not the primary source of resistance they were portrayed to be. However, they often accepted in an unquestioning manner the views put forward by various vested interests. This can create the impression that the politicians themselves are the source of the resistance, and not the lobby group.

Many politicians are suspicious of public servants, and perceive rightly or wrongly that public servants often have little regard for their capacity. They often believe that public servants are unwilling to seriously consider any of their suggestions. This lack of trust between public servants and politicians can make it much easier for various interest groups to convince politicians that the State, through the public service, is being unreasonable in their dealings with them. This can result in situations where public servants acting in the public interest find themselves having to battle politicians to achieve the best outcome.

I found it was possible to establish a constructive relationship with the majority of politicians across the political divide. Being willing to listen to political input to debates on healthcare is important. For example, it was important for the HSE to understand that while Dáil committees, especially the Public Accounts Committee, could be very challenging for the HSE, and for me as CEO, they also had a very significant and positive impact, through their analysis, on driving transformation.

Establishing good relationships with politicians also depended on getting out and meeting people on the ground across the country. When debating issues with politicians there was nothing more helpful than having knowledge of the services and the people who provided them in their local areas. Having such knowledge confirmed to politicians that there was respect for their community and their community's requirements at a central level in the organisation. Being able to show that you knew and were aware of the capacity of the managers in their local areas, had visited some of the healthcare centres in their constituencies and understood the geography in terms of distances from services, etc. built their confidence in your commitment to their communities.

At a government level, there was always serious concern about the pace at which transformation was being driven. Governments do not intentionally stall change programmes, but they do want them to advance at a pace that minimises opposition in the community. Unfortunately, driving public service transformation at a slow pace is probably what dooms most such transformation programmes. In a context where everybody knows that inefficient services do not go bankrupt powerful interest groups can align against public service transformation. Under such circumstances change that is slow will generally be effectively blocked.

We were faced with a situation where the Government, while it supported transformation, could not easily cope with the fact that change had to be brought about quickly, especially hospital reconfiguration. We understood the pressure that the Cabinet was under to try to slow these changes, but at the same time we knew that it was our responsibility as an organisation to drive the change programme forward. We had to operate as a Trojan horse, with the Government having the opportunity to blame us for the change.

Commercial Interests

As a single national agency, the HSE had to take responsibility and create opportunities for getting better value for money in terms of its commercial activities. This included achieving a reduction in the cost of all supplies and the provision of services such as banking, legal and telecommunication services. The companies involved in providing equipment and services for the HSE varied from some of the world's largest drug manufacturing companies to local bakeries. All of these were affected by the HSE managing its business in a way that was very different from the system under the health boards. The immediate response from several of those affected by such change, from the largest to the smallest, was understandably to seek political and public support in trying to stop the HSE from developing normal commercial interactions with its suppliers.

Logically, we might have expected the public to actively support this new approach to getting better value for taxpayers' money. However, each of these interest groups is very powerful at different levels. The pharmacy business has very deep pockets for political lobbying and running media campaigns. Small local businesses, such as construction companies, engineering works or taxis, are very effective at mounting local political and media campaigns.

The public regularly complain about waste and poor management by public service providers like the HSE, but when the system is professionally managed some complain about it being unfair. When the HSE was starting out, Ireland was in the midst of an economic boom and the public didn't identify reducing the price paid to a taxi company to bring a patient to hospital for an outpatient clinic or reducing the price paid to the local pharmacist for drugs as saving their money. Rather, they often saw it, and it was portrayed to them, as a bureaucracy operating in an unreasonable manner, locally and nationally.

Clinicians, Politicians and the Media

Politicians are often readily influenced by healthcare professionals who express their views in the media. We, as clinicians, tend to be trusted completely by the public and our commitment to improving healthcare is rarely challenged. However, as with every other group of workers, our views are influenced by the fact that changes in the provision of health services will impact on our day-to-day working environment and could make this environment more demanding for us. The absolute belief by the public and many politicians that the views of healthcare professionals – doctors, nurses and others – are consistently impartial and expressed only with a view to protecting patients can be very damaging to change programmes that are actually in the public's interest. This belief can result not only in politicians but in the media being remarkably responsive in an unquestioning manner to the opinions of professional lobbying groups.

An example of this was a *Prime Time Investigates* TV programme on RTÉ in 2010 on waiting times in hospital accident and emergency (A&E) departments. While in 2005 almost every A&E department in Ireland had significant numbers waiting for long periods, the HSE had now reached a point where the problem was largely confined to six hospitals. When informed that this programme was to be made, the HSE asked RTÉ, as the national public service broadcaster, to present on hospitals which had successfully dealt with this challenge as well as hospitals where problems still existed. We recommended Waterford Regional Hospital as an example of good practice. RTÉ had already identified Beaumont Hospital as the hospital they would use to show the problems that existed in A&E departments.

Waterford A&E is the second largest A&E in Ireland, with 60,000 annual attendances. Waiting times are always minimal because the management and clinical leaders are implementing highly effective clinical practices. These processes are based on many patients being immediately directed to a medical assessment unit where they are seen by a consultant physician rather than having to go through a full assessment by the clinicians in the A&E department before being referred to the consultant physician. Tests are carried out immediately, including X-rays and scans, because the medical assessment unit has priority access to the necessary facilities. Providing services in this way means that the need to admit the patient to hospital is, in many cases, eliminated. At the same time, the A&E department can focus on accidents and major emergencies, which is what it is designed to do.

In contrast, Beaumont Hospital traditionally had no such structure or processes in place, despite this system of care being a central part of the HSE transformation programme. All urgent patients referred to the hospital had to be first fully assessed in the A&E department, irrespective of the fact that many of them would have to be subsequently referred to a consultant physician for a repeat assessment and opinion. A lot of the time, the only way that the consultant physician's opinion could be obtained or investigations performed was by admitting the patient to hospital. This was in stark contrast to what happened many similar patients in Waterford, which is a busier A&E with a much inferior infrastructure.

RTÉ filmed in both units. The *Prime Time Investigates* programme broadcast less than one minute of the Waterford story and over ten minutes of the Beaumont story. There was no opportunity for the Waterford clinicians to explain their successful system of care. During the Beaumont segment, various professionals were interviewed who voiced many complaints about the health service. They were never asked why they did not provide their services in the way that was clearly so successful in Waterford. This would seem to have been a most obvious question in the public interest. However, as was generally the case, the opinions of healthcare professionals were not challenged.

To be fair to Beaumont Hospital, they now have excellent clinical leadership in place and their board is focused on putting in place a system similar to that in Waterford and other hospitals around the country. It should also be stated that Beaumont was no different to some other hospitals in Dublin, and a number of other hospitals across the country, in the way it operated its emergency services.

Chapter 6

The 3,000-Bed Plan

Prior to the establishment of the HSE, the Department of Health and Children carried out an analysis of the requirement for acute hospital beds in Ireland. This analysis, entitled *Acute Hospital Bed Capacity – A National Review* (2002), was done because of long waiting lists for elective procedures as well as the large number of emergency patients waiting for admission in A&E departments across the country. When issued, the report proposed that 3,000 more hospital beds were required to adequately provide acute hospital services in Ireland. This was widely welcomed by all stakeholders. The Irish economy was extremely buoyant at the time, and the costs associated with an increase of 3,000 beds, almost a 25 per cent increase in bed capacity, were not considered daunting. Overall, it was felt by all stakeholders, including the politicians, the Department, the public and health service representative groups, that this would provide the answer to many of the problems in the Irish healthcare system.

This proposal was very plausible, easily communicated and therefore difficult to challenge. However, the transformation programme that the HSE was proposing was focused on ensuring that people would receive more of their hospital-based care without actually having to be admitted to hospital. Hospitals and healthcare professionals would have to change the way they worked, providing rapid access for patients to senior clinical decision makers and to diagnostic tests through new medical and surgical assessment units. Admission to hospital would therefore be a last resort. The Government and the Department's plan to build 3,000 more beds and the HSE transformation plan were essentially two trains coming along the same track in opposite directions. Despite the plausibility of the 3,000-bed proposal and the widespread support for it, this was an issue that the HSE as an organisation had to confront. If the health service simply built more of the same structures to support the existing ways of delivering care to patients there was never going to be any hope of getting healthcare professionals to change the way they worked to provide services for the public in a much more coordinated way.

The potential economic impact of this proposal on the health services, and on Ireland as a country, was enormous, and yet there was no evidence based on international comparisons to justify the investment in more beds. The capital cost of building 3,000 beds, the equivalent of another six Dublin teaching hospitals, would have been between €2 and €3 billion, which would have to be added to the national debt. More alarmingly, the annual revenue costs would be over €1 billion per year. This massive investment would be further developing a system that was continuing to admit large numbers of people to hospital unnecessarily, for excessive periods of time.

I began to speak publicly about the need to stop the plan to add 3,000 new acute hospital beds and the associated infrastructure. This caused surprise as, historically, clinicians had always been seen as welcoming more beds. It led immediately to a disagreement between the HSE and some high profile stakeholder groups, including clinicians' representative bodies, and with some in the political system. It did, however, present an opportunity to highlight the HSE's transformation programme and drew people's attention for the first time to the fact that we were proposing radical change in the way services were provided, to create an integrated system focused on patients' needs.

The proposal for more beds was based on an evaluation that compared Ireland to other developed countries across the world in terms of the number of beds in acute hospitals. It did not include the number of private beds in Ireland, which increased the overall number of beds by 15–20 per cent. The study found that Ireland had practically the same number of acute hospital beds as the UK. If private beds were included, Ireland had a greater number of acute beds per 1,000 head of population than the UK.

There was no adjustment made for the very young age profile of the Irish population. In Ireland, only 11 per cent of the population were over sixty-five years of age, whereas in the UK 18 per cent were over sixty-five, and this figure was even higher in some European countries. This was a critical issue, as all health services spend a minimum of 70 per cent of their budget in providing care for people over sixty-five years of age. Ireland should therefore have had a far lower requirement for acute beds than the UK or Germany and, indeed, our overall expenditure on healthcare should have been significantly less than in these countries.

The evaluation had not carried out a detailed review of the average length of stay of patients with specific conditions in Irish hospitals. The average time spent in hospital by patients with most conditions was significantly longer in Ireland than in comparable countries. This longer average length of hospital stay pointed to inefficiencies in our hospital service. Such inefficiencies were essentially being rewarded as this was the justification for the recommendation that the taxpayer should make a further significant investment to build and staff 3,000 more beds. This was not just an issue of saving money but was critical to improving the quality of service provided to the public. All of us would much prefer to be at home rather than in hospital.

When the HSE was established and a detailed performance measurement system was put in place (see Chapter 13, Healthstat) we found that the length of time people spent in hospital for the same problem varied dramatically, not only between different hospitals, but within the same hospital. We found that a person admitted to hospital to have their appendix removed would stay for an average of three and a half days if admitted under the care of one surgeon, or seven days if admitted under another surgeon. These marked differences were replicated up and down the country for almost every condition. People with heart attacks could spend twice as long in hospital when admitted under one doctor compared with another. The same applied to patients being admitted to hospital for operations that could have been carried out as a day procedure. One surgeon could treat almost 100 per cent of patients with cataracts as day patients, preventing many of these elderly people from having to go through the frightening experience of hospital admission. Another surgeon would insist that all such patients were admitted to hospital, sometimes for two to three days. The length of time people stayed in hospital was longer for every specialty in Ireland than in comparable countries like the UK. This was not due to elderly long-stay patients, as they were excluded from the analysis.

Acute Hospital Bed Capacity – A National Review also did not assess the potential impact of enhancing community-based services on the overall health service and the requirement for more beds. This was a surprise, as across the world countries were beginning to focus on the requirement to move work from hospitals to the community.

One might imagine that providing such counterarguments to the 3,000-bed proposal would lead to significant questions among stakeholders as to the need to build the extra beds. There was a constructive response from the Government to this and a willingness by the Minister and her government colleagues to listen to the alternative that we were proposing. At a senior level in the Department of Health and Children there was also a willingness to accept that this was a constructive alternative view. However, among the other stakeholders, especially the representative bodies for nurses and doctors, and from hospitals across the system there was vehement opposition to any proposal that would stop this major building project for acute hospitals.

The pressure on the HSE was immense because, at the time of its establishment, almost all of the A&E departments had significant delays for patients awaiting admission. There were instances where I was portrayed as the only person in Ireland who believed that we did not, as a country, require more beds. People referred to our plans to transform the system of delivery, and not build 3,000 beds, as utopian. There was no acceptance that processes in the existing hospital system were inefficient. It was very easy for hospitals to maintain that they were efficient in the absence of detailed performance measures. When performance measurements were finally initiated in 2008, they showed huge disparities in efficiency within our hospitals and, indeed, the entire health service.

Hospitals in Ireland had always seen bed numbers as the major indicator of their importance in the world of healthcare. They felt threatened if the number of beds fell below those of a comparable hospital. In some respects, it is easy to understand this because the funding provided to hospitals tended to be global, and had very little association with the complexity or quality of care provided in the hospital. The biggest driver of funding was staff numbers and the number of beds in the hospital. It was not surprising, therefore, that hospitals were consistently trying to increase their number of beds.

In the absence of a performance measurement system that focused on effective processes from a patient's perspective, there was no incentive for hospitals to develop more efficient processes and thereby use their existing beds more efficiently. In fact, based on beds being the currency of the system, the opposite was the case. Making the system more effective from a patient's perspective, by reducing the length of time you waited for a test or a procedure in hospital, could cost the hospital money.

We were able to get sufficient support from the Minister and from her government colleagues as well as the Secretary General of the Department of Health and Children to ensure the plan for more beds did not advance at a rapid pace. This created time for us to develop more detailed performance measures, which ultimately allowed us to show clearly the inefficiencies that were in the healthcare service and the need to focus on improving the effectiveness of the service rather than building more of the same.

There was, however, a very protracted debate and every time a peak occurred in waiting times in A&E departments the argument about beds was resurrected and the HSE became a major target for criticism, having prevented the perceived solution to the problem. The only way to settle this argument was to get external validation of the acute bed requirements in Ireland.

The *Acute Hospital Bed Review*

The HSE, therefore, commissioned a comprehensive evaluation of Ireland's requirement for acute hospital beds. Without such a review, it was going to be impossible to continue to defend our position.

The study was carried out by an international consultancy company. It evaluated the need for acute hospital beds based on existing practices. It then assessed how many beds would be required if Irish hospitals adopted new ways of providing care, thereby reducing the length of time people spent in hospital. This would mean changes like daily consultant-led ward rounds and more rapid access to tests and X-rays, which were, in any event, going to be carried out at some stage during the patient's admission. It also noted that while some Irish hospitals were excellent at carrying out appropriate surgical operations as day procedures other hospitals had a dismal record in doing so, and unnecessarily admitted the vast majority of such patients. It reported that there was no discharge planning process put in place at the time of admission for 60 per cent of patients. This inevitably meant that many discharges were delayed, delays which could have been avoided if plans for discharge, including links with community services, were initiated at the time the patient was admitted.

At the time of this review in 2007, there were 11,660 acute beds in Irish public hospitals. Based on the existing practices, the review calculated that 12,778 beds were required at that time to provide for public demand. Furthermore, continuing with these practices would mean that, by 2020, we would require 19,882 beds to cope with increasing demand for services. The capital costs of building this infrastructure for 2020 was estimated at over €4 billion, and the revenue costs for running our hospital services would double. This was clearly unsustainable.

If we adopted radical new practices, increasing the amount of day surgery as well as reducing the length of stay for people admitted to hospital, and built extra long-term care beds and primary care teams, the effect would be very significant. Fully adopting a modern approach to providing care could reduce our requirement for acute hospital beds in 2020 from 19,882 to 8,834. The capital investment associated with this modern method of care delivery would be €540 million as against €4 billion, and operating annual costs would be reduced by over €10 billion. That these reductions in the required bed complement were achievable was confirmed by the fact that, in 2006, Australia, the UK, Finland, Denmark and Canada were delivering the same amount of activity in their health systems as Ireland, using between 2,000 and 5,000 less hospital beds depending on the country.

Perhaps the most powerful argument against building more hospital beds is to consider what the best scenario would be from a patient's perspective. I often stood in rooms with large numbers of clinicians, doctors and nurses who were arguing for more beds and asked the question: how many of them wanted to be in hospital for their care if it was at all possible to provide care as a day patient or outside of hospital? When people reflected on this question, they realised that what they were actually proposing was not consistent with providing healthcare services in a way that they themselves would want. While this argument was very effective in rooms full of clinicians, it did not reduce the fervent opposition to our strategy on beds by clinical commentators in the media. Such commentators seemed to be convinced that patients were best treated by being confined to hospital for their care. Or perhaps this simply presented the ideal model for them as clinicians. Ultimately, more beds meant investing more State funds in healthcare professionals and in hospitals.

The focus of the HSE in redirecting resources from building more acute beds to supporting and enhancing primary and community facilities also showed that the organisation would indirectly have an effect on healthcare policy. It was always going to be impossible to clearly distinguish policy development by the Government and the Department of Health and Children from implementation by the HSE. The debate on beds confirmed this for everybody, especially, I believe, for the Government, who ultimately saw some advantage of the delivery system having an input in policy development. In the absence of the HSE, Ireland would have committed huge funds to building hospitals which it did not need and could never afford to staff adequately, even in good economic times.

In 2011, it is hard to believe this argument on the need for more hospital beds ever took place. There is now widespread acceptance of the fact that our hospitals needed to, and have progressively become, more efficient – a trend that will continue. Those who were vehement advocates of an increase in hospital beds now regularly comment on more beds not being the solution but rather a continued improvement in the processes that operate in our hospitals. Such is change – according to Schopenhauer.

Chapter 7

Hospital Reconfiguration

A successful integrated healthcare system will provide as much care as possible to patients in their own local environment, at home and through primary care centres, rather than admitting people to hospitals. Developing this patient-orientated system depends on moving staff such as nurses and therapists to work in the community rather than hospitals.

As mentioned, hospital beds are extremely expensive for us as taxpayers, and none of us wants to be admitted to a hospital, if at all possible. You would therefore expect that reconfiguring the hospital services and reducing the number of beds would be both popular with the public and easy to achieve. Unfortunately, this is not the case. Local communities feel very threatened when they hear that their local hospital service is to undergo any change. This is because many believe that the hospital is the most important part of the healthcare service, and that people will die unnecessarily if services are removed from their local hospital.

In dealing with fears about changes in local hospital services, it is useful to consider the experience of communities that do not have a local hospital, and those that are a considerable distance from an acute hospital. First, we should consider the effect of not having a local hospital in terms of how long people live. Athlone is one of Ireland's largest towns and does not have an acute hospital. Similarly, Longford is a large town without an acute hospital. The mortality rates for people from the same socioeconomic group who live in Athlone or Longford are not any different from those of people who live in Dublin, Wexford, Ennis or Galway, or any town or city with an acute hospital. People in West Mayo who live sixty to seventy miles from their local hospital in Castlebar live as long as people who are resident in Castlebar. In an emergency such as an accident at work, or a road traffic accident, the critical factor in terms of survival is having highly trained ambulance staff to provide urgent care.

Living close to a hospital may potentially have adverse effects. People who live in Cork City are much more likely to be admitted to hospital than people who live in rural parts of Co. Cork. The same applies to people who live in Waterford City, who are much more likely to be admitted than those in rural parts of the county. Despite this, people in the cities of Cork and Waterford do not live longer than their rural counterparts.

The north-eastern region of Ireland had five acute hospitals for a population of almost 370,000 people. When we reviewed hospital admissions back in 2005, we found that people in the North East were up to twice as likely to be admitted to hospital as people in other parts of Ireland, or comparable parts of the UK. When the north-eastern area was compared to Dublin City's Northside, it was found that for every 100,000 people 37 were admitted each week to acute surgical units in the North East, compared to 19 per 100,000 people in North Dublin. There was no reason why appendicitis or any other surgical condition would be more common in the North East. This was confirmed by the fact that there was no increase in the number of surgical interventions carried out in the North East. A large number of patients admitted to the surgical wards in the North East had no surgery or any other procedure carried out. All of this confirms that the more hospitals and the more hospital beds that are available, the more likely people are to be admitted to hospital.

The findings in Ireland confirm Roemer's Law. Dr Milton Roemer was a renowned public health specialist and was a professor at the University of California, Los Angeles School of Public Health. He examined how the number of hospital beds per head of population influences hospitalisation rates. He and his colleagues found that an increase in available hospital beds in an area led to more people being admitted to hospital. Roemer's Law states that 'a hospital bed built is a hospital bed filled.' According to the Dartmouth Atlas Project, Roemer's Law can be stated as 'supply can induce its own demand where a third party practically guarantees reimbursement of usage.' In the US, this third party refers to insurance companies; in Ireland it is the taxpayer.

The need to reconfigure the Irish hospital services in terms of the number of hospitals providing 24-hour services had been obvious to clinicians and many politicians for years. Acute services were being provided across approximately fifty hospital sites (including speciality hospitals, and maternity and children's hospitals) for a population of 4.5 million people on a small island. Several reports, including the Hanly Report (2003), had pointed out that high quality services could not be provided through such a configuration of hospitals. Despite all of the evidence that had been produced supporting the need for reconfiguration over the previous twenty years few changes had been implemented.

The challenge for the HSE was to reconfigure hospital services in a way that would allow hospitals to provide the safest service possible for the population. Reconfiguring hospitals to provide safer services was always going to result in the HSE being portrayed as incompetent and uncaring by groups opposed to the change. However, the HSE had to proceed with the reconfiguration of hospitals, irrespective of the risks that were involved from the organisation's perspective. We could not afford to be part of a populist approach when independent reports had stated that people were receiving inadequate care because of how our hospitals were structured.

Presenting a reconfiguration plan for all the hospitals in the country would generate resistance at a national level from many groups. Therefore, like most previous attempts to implement reconfiguration at a national level, it would fail. We made a decision that reconfiguration would be planned on an area-by-area basis. To achieve this in a way that was credible, we got international experts to review the structure of our hospital services in a number of areas. They proposed, based on the size of the population and the geography of the area, what the optimal configuration of hospitals should be.

One of our goals in planning reconfiguration at a regional level was to be able to demonstrate to the local population and local politicians the need for change in their own area if services were to become as safe as possible. We measured activity in individual hospitals and pointed out the significant risks that were associated with low levels of activity from a patient's perspective. Measuring the actual work that was happening in a hospital allowed us to counter the arguments against reconfiguration of hospital services with facts and figures. For example, many communities believed that their local hospital was significantly overworked. While this was true in some cases, many of these hospitals were not nearly as busy or overworked as was portrayed. Public representatives were generally surprised at how little activity there actually was in smaller hospitals, especially at night, considering the numbers of doctors, nurses and other staff employed.

Reconfiguration in the North East

An example of the configuration of hospitals kept in place by the old health board structure was the North East, which included the counties of Cavan, Monaghan, Louth and Meath. This area had a population of 370,000 and five acute hospitals on call each night. While maternity and obstetric services were provided on only two sites, general medical and surgical services were provided on all sites. Over the previous twenty-five years, attempts had been made to reconfigure services in the North East, which was under the old system a single health board area. Under the old health board structure, politicians on the board supported their local hospital and all ultimately became aligned in ensuring that no change would take place. While many of the executives did strive to bring about reconfiguration, they were undermined by the political nature of the health board structure. From the local politicians' perspective, arguments about quality of care were of interest, but ultimately there had to be a recognition that the local hospital was often the largest employer in a town.

A sad event resulted in our decision to focus on the reconfiguration of these hospitals in the north-eastern part of the country to begin with: the death of a patient in late 2005 at Monaghan General Hospital. Monaghan General Hospital was a small hospital, providing acute medical and surgical services to a catchment area of 50,000 people. The patient had been transferred earlier from Our Lady of Lourdes Hospital, Drogheda, where he had been treated for bleeding in his stomach following a hip replacement operation. Overnight at Monaghan General he had a recurrence of significant bleeding in his stomach. Following initial attempts to treat him at Monaghan General Hospital, it became apparent that it was going to be impossible to provide adequate support for him and attempts were made to transfer him back to Drogheda. There were inadequate operating procedures for the transfer of acute emergencies between hospitals in the region at the time. Each hospital operated as an independent acute unit. Therefore Our Lady of Lourdes Hospital considered that, if required, the patient should be transferred to Cavan General Hospital, which was closer to Monaghan General. The patient died while discussions on transferring him to Drogheda or Cavan continued between the three hospitals.

This was an unacceptable situation. Here was a man who developed a major complication in what was a designated surgical centre, but it was clear that his stomach bleeding could not be managed in this unit. Nevertheless, the hospital remained open as an acute care facility for medicine and surgery.

When these incidents are highlighted the problem is that individual clinicians within the hospital see it as an attack on their clinical competence, which confuses the argument. This is not a question of the competence of the clinicians who work in smaller hospitals. No clinician, regardless of their expertise, can be expected to provide adequate care without comprehensive support structures such as intensive care and a full array of diagnostic services that are required to support such care. These services cannot be provided in smaller hospitals, not only because of the cost, but because there is not sufficient activity to maintain the skills of clinicians.

Following this man's untimely death, we at the HSE committed immediately to carrying out an evaluation of acute hospital services in the north-eastern region and to plan future developments according to best international practice. A UK-based international consultancy firm, Teamwork Management Services, carried out the evaluation. The first part of Teamwork's evaluation was to determine activity levels in each of the acute hospitals. Their findings were dramatic. The figures showed that the number of patients admitted to hospitals in the region was significantly in excess of what would be expected for the size of the population.

At the same time, the HSE was carrying out a review of patients in the acute hospitals in Ireland to determine if the patients needed to be in hospital. This review was carried out using a standard international methodology. In the five north-eastern hospitals, 55 per cent of the patients did not need to be in an acute hospital bed.

The Teamwork report also confirmed that the level of activity in cardiac care and intensive care units was so low across the sites that it was impossible to provide the best possible care for very ill patients. There were indications that the public in the area were aware of this. Almost 40 per cent of people who lived in the catchment area of the hospitals in the North East travelled to Dublin for services. This highlights another interesting issue in reconfiguration, which is the contradiction between the public's determination to maintain local services while many of them use services in other areas.

The Teamwork report proposed that the five hospitals in the North East should be amalgamated and one new hospital built to provide all services for the population of the North East. The logic for this was clear. It would create a centre which would have adequate activity to provide all acute care services. Most importantly, it would have an adequate workload to justify comprehensive intensive care and coronary care units, allowing it to provide safe services for those who were critically ill. It would also allow for the establishment of services that were not developed in the region at this time. These included ear, nose and throat, and ophthalmology (eye) services.

There was a remarkably muted response to Teamwork's report, considering that it was proposing that four of the five 24-hour acute hospitals in the North East would no longer exist. The site for the new hospital had not been identified and most people considered that their area could be competitive as the site for the hospital. This presented an opportunity to gain acceptance of the principle that there was a need for rationalisation in terms of the number of acute hospitals.

Following the publication of Teamwork's report, we engaged with local politicians and national politicians to sell the concept of a reconfiguration. There was significant agreement among politicians on this need for change, and also on the need to provide services in the area that were presently only available in Dublin.

A group was set up by the HSE to study the demography and geography of the area and then identify a location for the new hospital. Ultimately, this group identified the town of Navan, which was the site of one of the smallest hospitals in the North East, as the proposed location for the new hospital. Once a specific location had been identified, the widespread support for reconfiguration of the acute hospitals in the area immediately dissipated. Politicians and clinicians from all of the other locations in the North East put forward multiple reasons as to why services in existing hospitals could not be transferred to Navan.

For the HSE, the problem was that we did not have funding to build the new hospital. Therefore, there was a danger that, having chosen Navan as the ideal site, it would be several years before funding was available and, in the meantime, the status quo would continue while we waited to implement the ideal solution.

Because of the risk of having to continue to provide services in a totally inadequate way for several years, the HSE decided to proceed with the rationalisation of acute services by moving them from the five sites to two existing hospital sites, one in the north (Cavan) and one in the south of the region (Drogheda). These were the two largest hospitals in the region, which had obstetric and paediatric services as well as acute medical and surgical services. In addition, the HSE developed a plan to promote a more rapid rollout of the primary care team infrastructure in the area. This was very challenging because many GPs were vehemently opposed to any reduction in the number of acute hospital sites and especially to the removal of A&E services. They were therefore hesitant to support the development of primary care teams for the area. A plan was also put in place to greatly enhance the ambulance services across the area.

In the absence of clinical leadership it was going to be extremely difficult for the HSE to deliver on this reconfiguration plan. Unfortunately, many clinicians in the area were demoralised, based on a long history of failure to deliver on proposals for change. They were frustrated by the fact that their services had never been adequately developed, while significant money that should have come to the North East was invested in improving services in Dublin, based on Dublin hospitals providing services for patients from the North East.

The HSE established a reconfiguration steering group and we assigned a senior manager from our Finance Directorate, Mr Stephen Mulvany, to lead this process of reconfiguration. It was a thankless task, especially in the absence of clinical leadership. We asked an eminent Dublin-based cardiovascular surgeon, Professor Eilis McGovern, to undertake a clinical leadership role. She and Stephen decided to focus initially on bringing about reconfiguration in the northern part of the region. This involved acute services at Monaghan being moved to Cavan. They would then proceed with moving acute services from the two smaller hospitals in the south (Navan and Dundalk) to Drogheda. They developed a detailed project-based approach to the overall programme of change in the region and I actively engaged with the steering group in an attempt to get more local clinical buy-in.

One of the important learning outcomes from this approach was that Stephen Mulvany quickly realised that you could plan a change programme and set up projects to implement the changes, but little was likely to happen unless you controlled the day-to-day funding of services. This was something that I had misjudged. I believed that a reconfiguration programme could operate independently of day-to-day service provision. We, therefore, gave Stephen Mulvany control of the hospital budget and the day-to-day running of services for the north-eastern region, as well as responsibility for reconfiguration. This had a positive effect in that it allowed him to use the lever of budgets to bring about change, and also brought him into daily contact with local clinicians.

Monaghan General Hospital was the first hospital to have its overnight services in acute surgery, acute medicine and A&E discontinued. It became a focus for all who opposed hospital reconfiguration across Ireland. There were major marches in Monaghan Town, which drew the national media's attention to the reconfiguration agenda. The local Hospital Action Committee was successful in using this exposure in the national media to raise concerns about the potential impact on small hospitals in other towns across the country. The most powerful resistance, however, came from local clinicians, especially local GPs, who had credibility when they appeared in the national media. They portrayed scenarios such as patients dying because of the lack of rapid access to local acute services. It is obvious that the interests of GPs, on a personal level, are never served by the withdrawal of A&E services from their area. A&E services provide a very comprehensive support mechanism for local GPs in terms of direct access for patients to overnight care and their withdrawal is always going to place greater demands on GPs for the provision of overnight services.

It was extremely difficult to bring about reconfiguration of services in an environment where we were being challenged by clinicians. The media accepted any input from doctors and nurses as being totally in the best interest of the patient. They didn't dig deeper to examine any of the personal issues that perhaps underlay such strenuous opposition.

Some of the resistance to change, based on the fact that services at Cavan General Hospital and Our Lady of Lourdes Hospital were already overstretched, was understandable. The provision of acute services across five sites meant that, while there were adequate numbers of physicians, surgeons and nurses in the area as a whole, no individual site had a sufficient number of clinicians to provide a comprehensive service. Therefore, we made a decision to invest approximately €80 million in the infrastructure at Our Lady of Lourdes, which for years had been in need of further development. This investment was to allow for the development of a new A&E department and seventy new beds, as well as new intensive care and coronary care units. In contrast, the infrastructure at Cavan General Hospital was modern and therefore only required minor redevelopment to provide the required resources there. The HSE also proceeded with the development of medical assessment units, which provide rapid access to senior decision makers for patients referred by GPs, without the need for hospital admission. We also committed to a major enhancement of ambulance services across the region.

The decision to invest significant funds, especially in Our Lady of Lourdes Hospital and in the ambulance service, was important in proving that the HSE was committed to real change on this occasion as opposed to the many failed plans for reconfiguration that had been discussed over the previous twenty years. However, there was a continued lack of significant input from clinicians locally and Eilis McGovern and Stephen Mulvany found it very challenging to get widespread clinical support for reconfiguration.

By late 2007 we had concerns that reconfiguration in the North East was not going to be achieved, especially in the absence of local clinical leadership to drive it forward. Failure of this reconfiguration project could significantly undermine the entire transformation programme of the HSE. We would be portrayed as having backed down in the face of political pressure, as had happened consistently in the past.

Reconfiguration in the Mid-West

The HSE decided to open up a second front by initiating a reconfiguration programme for hospitals and community services in the mid-western region. We chose the Mid-West as an area because we believed we had an excellent chance of delivering change there and, hopefully, if we succeeded, this would accelerate the change programme in the North East and bring focus on the need for change elsewhere in the country.

The specific reasons why we made a significant commitment to reconfiguration in the Mid-West are easy to describe. There were four hospitals across the mid-western region, covering a population of approximately 350,000. The big difference between the Mid-West and the North East was that there was one hospital with almost 500 beds at the Mid-Western Regional Hospital in Limerick City, which was far larger than the smaller hospitals in Ennis, Co. Clare, Nenagh in North Tipperary and St John's in Limerick City. Furthermore, the Mid-Western Regional Hospital was geographically situated in the centre of the region. Finally, and most importantly, we were aware that there were excellent clinical leaders in the mid-western region who, if we could convince them to engage with the project, were likely to become drivers of change.

Teamwork was again engaged to carry out an evaluation of the mid-western region. Their findings were similar to those in the North East, except that the one large hospital, Limerick's Mid-Western Regional Hospital, had significant levels of speciality expertise already in place and could provide comprehensive services for the area if adequately resourced. Teamwork confirmed again that activity across the other three sites was extremely low, and that significant resources were tied up in maintaining 24-hour services that could never achieve adequate quality because of the low throughput.

Acute surgical units were open twenty-four hours a day in all four hospitals, with a full complement of surgeons and operating theatre staff on call. Both Nenagh and Ennis admitted an average of three emergency surgical patients per day. The activity levels in Ennis, Nenagh and St John's Hospital in Limerick City were so low that, on average, only one emergency surgical case per week required surgery outside normal daytime working hours in these hospitals. The costs associated with maintaining these services, including large amounts of overtime payments, were significant. The A&E departments operated more like primary care facilities than emergency departments. The average A&E attendance per night between 8.00 p.m. and 8.00 a.m. was seven patients in Nenagh and nine in Ennis. The vast majority of these patients were self-referrals, who could have been much more appropriately managed by a GP out-of-hours service.

All of these hospitals were within a thirty-minute drive of the major hospital in the region – the Mid-Western Regional Hospital in Limerick. Despite their low levels of activity, they required a significant number of staff to provide 24-hour emergency cover. For example, Ennis Hospital, with 88 beds, had a staff of 291, including 32 doctors and 130 nurses.

While the cost of maintaining such services was prohibitive, the even bigger challenge was to maintain high quality services. Any hospital providing emergency services has to have the capacity within its intensive care unit to support critically ill patients. The intensive care units of Ennis, Nenagh and St John's Hospital had levels of activity that were too low to maintain the necessary skills of those working in the units. Providing artificial ventilation (breathing) support for patients is one of the most important functions of an intensive care unit. The intensive care units in the three hospitals were providing ventilation support on average only 12 per cent of the time, compared to 90–100 per cent in fully functional intensive care units. The low levels of activity in the surgical, A&E and intensive care units could not have been considered compatible with the provision of the highest quality care. These units were dependent on the commitment of a small number of experienced consultants to maintain their services. It would have been impossible to maintain this level of commitment in the future.

The recommendation of the Teamwork review was to consolidate most of the 24-hour services at the Mid-Western Regional Hospital. They pointed out that the Regional Hospital would need significant ongoing investment to manage the change. Equally, there was a need for the other hospitals in the area to provide increased day surgery and diagnostic services.

The HSE immediately began discussions on the reconfiguration plan with local clinical leaders, not just with doctors but also with nurses and Allied Health Professionals. We did not publish the report while these discussions were taking place. As CEO, I was engaged on a day-to-day basis in trying to bring about a commitment by local clinical leaders to this programme of change.

One of the first challenges we faced, as in the North East, was dealing with the fact that criticism of the services in the smaller hospitals was interpreted as criticism of the clinicians' skills and the quality of care they provided. This was impossible to avoid, but was unfortunate as many of these clinicians were extremely committed to providing the highest standards of care. I could identify with them as I knew, from personal experience working in the area in the past, how committed they were to providing the best possible care.

Following initial discussions on the plan, Mr Paul Burke, a vascular surgeon who operated across the two hospital sites in Limerick City, St John's Hospital and the Regional Hospital, and who was held in high regard by his colleagues, agreed to take on the role of clinical leader for the reconfiguration project. Paul Burke was and remains extremely committed to the mid-western region. He understood that clinicians in the Mid-West were not able to provide all the services that they should for the population because of the configuration of the hospital system. He was aware that many patients travelled to Galway, Cork and Dublin for services that could and should have been provided locally if services were properly configured, ensuring that the money invested in the services was used in the most effective way.

Initially, Paul's commitment was to reconfigure surgical and A&E services, including the ambulance services, and he did not see himself undertaking a reconfiguration of medical or, indeed, primary and community care services. However, before long he recognised that reconfiguration required change in all services because of their interdependencies. He became actively involved in leading the entire clinical transformation project for the region.

Paul Burke established his credibility locally by adopting a challenging approach to the HSE management, in terms of our commitment to supporting reconfiguration and willingness to invest where this was required in the reconfiguration programme. He, however, maintained an equally honest approach in pointing out locally that significant resources would be freed up by changing the way services were provided in local hospitals, and that these resources could then be reinvested in developing more comprehensive services for the region as a whole. The HSE committed to investing in the development of new intensive care, coronary care and cardiac intervention facilities on the site of the Regional Hospital. This confirmed that the reconfiguration programme could enhance overall services for the region. He was very successful in working with his clinical colleagues in the smaller hospitals who were most affected by the reconfiguration. While he was never going to be able to obtain support from all of them, he did manage to get the support of the majority of these clinicians. Most GPs based around the smaller hospitals, however, remained staunchly opposed to the reconfiguration programme in the Mid-West.

Because of his clinical background, Paul Burke was able to develop plans fairly quickly to centralise 24-hour A&E services and acute surgical services. He was also able to ensure that his colleagues on the central site in the Mid-Western Regional Hospital committed to moving elective surgical day services to the smaller sites. This was essential to free up capacity in Limerick to accommodate the extra acute work that would come from stopping emergency surgery on the other three sites. Achieving change like this on the ground was only possible through clinical leadership and it rapidly enhanced the credibility of the programme.

One of the most important roles for clinical leaders is the use of communications. In the north-eastern region we had some clinicians using the national media very effectively in opposing reconfiguration. This also occurred in the Mid-West, but such arguments were countered rapidly and effectively by Paul Burke and also by a number of his clinical colleagues who agreed to take part in media and public debates on reconfiguration. Some of the greatest sensitivity centred around the removal of A&E services from smaller hospitals. Dr Cathal O'Donnell, an A&E consultant in the Mid-West, was extremely effective in pointing out to the public that the A&E services that were being removed from their local hospitals were, in any event, not adequate services, and never could be, based on the size of the population they served.

While clinical leadership is essential for reconfiguring hospital services, it also requires courageous managers to work alongside clinicians. In the case of the Mid-West, it was important to the success of the project that Mr John O'Brien returned to Limerick as executive leader for the reconfiguration project. John had been a senior executive in the region before moving to work in the corporate offices of the HSE. John and Paul Burke had a very good working relationship. This alignment of strong executive and clinical leadership is ultimately the most vital component of a change programme like this, and the strength of the relationship is probably the best indicator of whether or not a programme will succeed. Also, the trust that existed between John O'Brien, the executive leader for the reconfiguration, and the senior executive responsible for service delivery, Mr John Hennessy, meant that they managed to avoid territorial battles and everybody focused on the greater good in terms of improving service provision.

The reconfiguration project was established in the Mid-West without the Teamwork report being published. This was subsequently released to the press by the Labour Party. This could have undermined the project due to the fear that was generated in local communities about moving services. However, the fact that the project was now up and running and, most importantly, that the clinical leaders were clear about their goals meant that there was a very different outcome. Following the leaking of the report, the clinical leaders immediately appeared on local and national media defending the reconfiguration project, which resulted in any negative response from local politicians being muted. In fact, national and local politicians from the Government parties were very constructive and felt that they could now support change in a context where they had clinical leaders to support them locally in explaining the reasons for change. While this reassurance of the public by clinicians did not make everyone happy, it led to a much more honest debate. Clinicians who are initially more than willing to appear in the national and local media opposing the reconfiguration of services are much less inclined to do so when they know that their arguments are going to be challenged by other clinicians.

Effects of Developments in the Mid-West on the North East

The fact that clinical leadership in the Mid-West successfully initiated the change programme had a major impact in the North East. It was more obvious than ever that, without local clinical leadership on the ground, it would be impossible to deliver the changes required there. We were at the same time having to cope with the fact that Eilis McGovern, the external clinical leader in the North East, was going to have to withdraw from her commitment there because of her appointment as vice president of the Royal College of Surgeons in Ireland.

We sought to identify another external leader and were extremely fortunate in recruiting Dr Colm Quigley, a consultant physician in the South East. Colm was a former president of the Medical Council and a former president of the Irish Hospital Consultants Association. He understood the need for and was hugely committed to change in the Irish health service. He also had great interpersonal skills and an enthusiasm that impacted those around him. His engagement brought significant credibility to the project and reassurance to government ministers from the North East that they had a strong clinical advocate to support them in explaining the need for the reconfiguration of services.

Clinicians in the North East were now aware of the progress that was being made in the reconfiguration of services in the Mid-West. There was a sense that the HSE had become frustrated by the failure to advance change at an adequate pace in the North East and was moving its focus elsewhere. There was also a realisation that an opportunity might be lost and clinicians would be left to continue with the status quo for the next twenty years if they did not adopt a more proactive approach themselves. The actions of the clinical leaders in the Mid-West and Colm Quigley's arrival allowed clinical leaders in the north-eastern region to see that it was possible as a clinician to lead change, despite significant opposition from some of your colleagues to the change programme and to the HSE. This led to the emergence of two excellent clinical leaders: Dr Dominic O'Brannigan in the south of the region and Dr James Hayes in Cavan/ Monaghan. Colm Quigley was able to work with both of them to develop broader clinical support on the ground for the change programme. Stephen Mulvany, as the executive lead, who must have felt he had been pushing a train up a hill for two or three years, was finally in a position to move forward much more expeditiously with the overall change programme. The detailed planning work that Stephen and Eilis McGovern had carried out actually resulted in a situation where the change programme was now able to move forward rapidly.

What Has Changed?

There are many in the North East and Mid-West who still say that little change has actually occurred. As always, it is difficult to accept that change of this magnitude is slow and that real change, by its very nature, is seldom identifiable as it is occurring. However, it is interesting to reflect on what has happened in both areas in comparison to what had happened in the previous forty years.

In the North East, almost all acute emergency surgery is now carried out on two rather than five sites. Medical assessment units have opened in Cavan, Navan and Drogheda, providing immediate access for patients referred by their GP to senior physicians as well as the necessary investigations, without having to be admitted to hospital. A major new capital development has been put in place in Our Lady of Lourdes Hospital, Drogheda including the development of state-of-the-art cardiac care and A&E departments. Perhaps most importantly, a highly skilled ambulance service staffed with advanced paramedics is now in place across the region. People with major illnesses like a heart attack or stroke, or who are involved in accidents, can now receive immediate on-the-spot life-saving treatment from these advanced paramedics. Advanced paramedics can carry out medical interventions up to and including the establishment of artificial ventilation – interventions which, in the past, would have been considered only possible in a hospital intensive care unit. The patient having been stabilised, the team then transport him or her to the major hospital in the area.

Under the old pre-reconfiguration system, an accident victim or patient with a heart attack would be brought to the local hospital, having received little apart from minor support. On arrival at the hospital, the patient would be stabilised and on occasions he or she was then placed back in an ambulance and transferred to a larger regional hospital for further treatment. Of course, time is of the essence in saving lives following a heart attack or accident. Immediate and appropriate care by advanced paramedics at the scene is critical to saving lives. While I have no doubt the public and clinicians in the North East continue to be frustrated by the pace of change, the changes that have happened have improved the care patients receive.

In the Mid-West, major change has occurred. All emergency surgery is now carried out on one site, not four sites as happened previously. A&E services have been centralised and, as in the North East, a excellent ambulance service is in place. New intensive care, cardiac care and cardiac intervention departments have been established in the region, and new diagnostic services, especially in radiology, have been put in place. Because clinicians are leading this change they have achieved reforms that were previously considered impossible, and which greatly enhance the quality of service they provide for people in their area.

Would any of these changes have been possible if the HSE had not been established? Evidence from the past would suggest not. It was and would always be almost impossible for a healthcare system operated by the Department of Health and Children to change the hospital services in this way, because of political influence and the pressure of electoral expediency. The HSE was able to take decisions in the public interest without the need to consider the electoral concerns of politicians.

Where Does Hospital Reconfiguration Go from Here?

The Government became concerned in 2008 about the speed at which reconfiguration was happening. As a result, the HSE was instructed not to carry out any further independent assessments on acute hospital services in specific areas unless this was sanctioned by a new committee to be established by the Department of Health and Children. The committee was never established.

Prior to the government decision to stop the HSE doing independent reviews, the HSE had completed such a review for the Cork/Kerry region, and, based on this, initiated a reconfiguration programme in 2009. In the Cork/Kerry region, which has a population of 620,000, Professor John Higgins is the clinical leader, working with Mr Pat Healy, the regional director of operations for the HSE Southern Area. They are implementing a change programme, again based on an external review carried out by Teamwork. The challenges they face are similar to those in the Mid-West and North East, but the combination of executive and clinical leadership will again, I believe, result in changes now happening that should have occurred years ago.

Similar reconfiguration of services is required in other areas, and plans are at various stages of development. The challenge of bringing about change without external validation of the need for such change is demonstrated in the south-eastern area, incorporating Waterford, Wexford, Carlow, Kilkenny and South Tipperary. Here, a local steering group, comprising HSE management, doctors, nurses and therapists, has been trying to develop a plan for reconfiguration, without the aid of an external or independent assessment of existing services.

The South East has four acute hospitals for a population of 460,000. The largest hospital is located in Waterford City, which unfortunately, unlike Limerick's central location, is at the periphery of the catchment area. However, the new road network has changed arguments around reconfiguration, as travelling times to Waterford from surrounding areas have been greatly reduced.

Outside Waterford, the three other hospitals at Wexford, Kilkenny, and Clonmel (South Tipperary) are relatively equal in size. Each of these hospitals provides acute medical and surgical services as well as obstetric and paediatric services. Each operates 24-hour A&E and surgical services. However, between midnight and 8.00 a.m., the A&E departments of the three hospitals combined see an average of thirteen patients each night, varying from three to five patients for each hospital. Overnight surgery occurs on average seven times a week across the three hospitals combined, varying between one and three surgical cases per hospital per week. There are eight junior doctors on call providing overnight cover in the surgical departments of the three hospitals. It is not an option to continue to provide services in this way. However, it is almost impossible for local management and clinicians to agree to a rationalisation programme. In Ireland, external reports are always required to support change of this significance. I believe it was a mistake not to carry out a full external review of services in the South East, the recommendations of which could have allowed local management and clinicians to implement the required changes, even in the face of political and other stakeholder opposition.

In the West, Dr David O'Keefe, as the clinical leader, and John Hennessy, as the regional director of operations for HSE West, have focused on reconfiguring the hospitals in Galway and Roscommon. Unfortunately, again there was no formal external review. There was significant concern in the local community and among staff in Roscommon Hospital about our proposal to remove 24-hour surgical services and the A&E department from the hospital. At meetings with management, senior clinicians and local politicians in Roscommon Hospital, I presented figures on activity at the hospital. At that time, the hospital had 84 beds and 330 staff, including 32 doctors and 120 nurses. On average, thirteen patients were admitted each day. In the A&E department there was an average of three attendances per night between midnight and 9.00 a.m. Overnight surgery almost never occurred. There was an average of three major surgical operations, including appendectomies, each week. At the same time, the overtime bill for junior doctors was €25,000 per week, and payment for locum staff to cover annual leave cost a further €10,000 per week.

The quality and cost implications are again obvious. How can patients be asked to have emergency surgery at night in a hospital when overnight surgery is carried out less than once a month, and where the significant surgical activity amounts to three or four cases per week?

In some respects, it is unfair to focus on the activity levels of the hospitals detailed here. These have been commented on because they are in areas undergoing reconfiguration. However, these hospitals are not any different to many hospitals across the country where activity levels are similarly low. It is remarkable that Ireland finds itself conducting debates about how to recruit enough doctors to staff over thirty A&E departments across the country when the real debate should be about how Ireland can justify having so many emergency departments, in terms of the quality of care patients receive and in terms of the quality of training junior doctors receive. As a result of recent increases in the number of Irish students entering medical schools, Ireland will soon be producing young doctors far in excess of the numbers required to staff our hospitals. However, this will not solve the problem because these young doctors will never take up positions in A&Es and other departments that are far too small to provide them with adequate training. Doctors and well-off patients vote with their feet and move elsewhere for services and training. Unfortunately, some patients do not have this luxury.

The Health Information and Quality Authority (HIQA) can be a powerful influence in bringing about reconfiguration of hospitals. It was a surprise that HIQA never commented on the need for reconfiguration of the Irish hospital system prior to the HSE undertaking the reconfiguration programmes in the North East and the Mid-West. Remarkably, HIQA made no comment in support of reconfiguration until it was asked by Minister Mary Harney to carry out a review on Ennis Hospital, following the leaking by the Labour Party of the plan for reconfiguration in the Mid-West. She wanted to have confirmation that the HSE's approach was correct. HIQA subsequently issued a report which confirmed the recommendations of the Teamwork report and fully supported the HSE's reconfiguration project. These changes were well underway by then, led by the clinical leaders in the Mid-West. It would have been of huge benefit if HIQA had expressed support for the changes during the difficult early days of establishing the reconfiguration projects in the North East and the Mid-West when the HSE was being severely criticised.

HIQA issued subsequent reports criticising the HSE for not having rapidly reconfigured hospitals all across the country. It would be great if such change could be achieved by simply issuing an edict, but the reality is very different, not only in Ireland, but in other healthcare systems. Any suggestion that change of this nature is easily achieved ignores the major public and political resistance, and the resistance of some healthcare professionals to such change. The reconfiguration of hospital services in an area requires a formal change programme, in conjunction with developing a cadre of skilled clinical leaders to implement it. This requires patience and tenacity.

Going forward, HIQA can play a critical role in supporting reconfiguration. As a regulator, HIQA needs to develop assessment metrics which support the change agenda to develop a quality integrated healthcare system. In its role as a regulator, HIQA is in a very powerful position to overcome resistance to change. It is important that the regulator and the HSE are working closely and supporting each other to achieve the changes required.

The introduction of a national insurance scheme, which I am not advocating, would also promote the reconfiguration of our hospitals. Insurance systems pay hospitals based on activity, and many hospitals, because of their relatively low activity levels, would find it very difficult within such a system to generate sufficient income to maintain the staffing levels required to deliver a 24-hour service.

For forty years prior to the establishment of the HSE, no change had taken place in the configuration of hospitals outside of Dublin. Going forward, the alignment of clinical leadership with health service management will, I believe, continue to bring about major improvements in the quality of services through reconfiguration. The big challenge will be avoiding a resurgence of political interference in the process. If this begins to happen, the clinicians and the managers may understandably withdraw to where they were pre-HSE, sitting back and washing their hands of any responsibility for the mess.

Chapter 8

Reconfiguring the Children's Hospitals

Just as reconfiguration of the hospital system in general is an essential component of improving the quality of healthcare in Ireland, the reconfiguration of the children's hospitals in Dublin was vital if we were to provide the best quality of care for seriously ill children in Ireland. There are three children's hospital services in Dublin. Our Lady's Children's Hospital, Crumlin is the major specialist centre for paediatrics in Ireland, also providing general paediatric services for children in Dublin. The Children's University Hospital, Temple Street, which is about half the size of Our Lady's Children's Hospital, also provides general and some specialist services. The smaller National Children's Hospital was the oldest children's hospital in the world and was based in the city centre. Over ten years ago, the National Children's Hospital moved as a children's wing to a new adult general hospital development in Tallaght, a suburb of Dublin.

The way the children's hospitals in Dublin are configured means that children cannot be provided with the best possible care, no matter how hard individual professionals try to do so. The three children's hospitals provide services such as paediatric surgery on three different campuses, despite the fact that the workload on some of the campuses is significantly below what is optimal to maintain the skills required to provide the service. This also applies to other services, such as intensive care, which require a minimum volume of work to maintain the skills of the professionals who provide them. Despite this, there has never been a proposal put forward voluntarily by any of the three hospitals or their boards that they would transfer a service to another hospital in order to improve the quality of the overall service.

In 1991, I was appinted as Professor of Paediatrics at UCD and Consultant Paediatric Gastroenterologist at Our Lady's Children's Hosptial, Crumlin. In 1995, I spoke at a meeting in Dublin organised by the Association for the Welfare of Children in Hospital (now called Children in Hospital Ireland (CHI)), an organisation whose goal is to ensure that the best possible care is provided for children in hospital. The meeting was well attended by representatives from Ireland and other European countries. I pointed out that the three children's hospitals appeared, by their inaction, to be more concerned about their own preservation than achieving the best possible care for children. While the comments generated a great deal of debate, much of it critical of my view, they signalled the start of a discussion that had to take place.

Individual clinicians within the hospitals accepted the need for consolidation. However, there was no appetite to take on a change programme that would have resulted in hospitals giving up some of their services. Maintaining the status quo in three hospitals avoided conflict or the need to make difficult decisions and was the easiest option for most of the stakeholders. However, it could never have been seen as the best option for children.

By 2000, it was clear that consolidation of the children's hospitals in Dublin to create a national centre of excellence for children's care was not going to happen if it depended on the individual hospitals agreeing to change. It was equally clear that the political system and the Department of Health and Children were never going to engage in promoting such a project while the three children's hospitals were opposed to such change.

When I began to consider what other approach could be taken, I realised that we had failed to engage the most important stakeholders in the debate. We had ignored the group that was most affected by the suboptimal configuration of services for children – the children themselves and their families.

In 2001, we sought the support of the parents of children who were using the services at Our Lady's Children's Hospital. Ideally, we would have brought together parents from across the three children's hospitals, but there was a risk that this would immediately create divisions between parents from the different hospitals. We had to hope that if we managed to create the case for a new children's hospital to replace the largest one – Our Lady's Children's Hospital – that this would initiate an honest debate on the provision of complex specialist services for all children in the country.

We asked consultants in various specialities in the hospital to identify parents who might be willing to participate. We invited these parents to a meeting at the hospital to discuss the issue of redeveloping the hospital or building a new hospital. Of approximately 100 people invited, over 70 attended – an encouraging turnout, considering that a lot of these were the parents of children with significant underlying medical conditions, and had many other demands on their time.

The group moved swiftly to appoint a committee and named itself the New Crumlin Hospital Group. The committee was composed of individuals with very varied backgrounds, including business executives, a journalist and mothers working in the home. They operated in a remarkably professional manner, under the chairmanship of Mr Karl Anderson. It was their belief that they could only operate effectively if they were not a lobby group for specific vested interests. They immediately established their independence from both me and the hospital board and executive. They engaged an international expert, Dr Ronald Pollock, to carry out an evaluation of the infrastructure at Our Lady's Children's Hospital. He produced what became known as the Pollock Report, which was clear in its evaluation that the hospital was not fit for purpose and had to be rebuilt. Using this document, the committee began to lobby the Government to rebuild Our Lady's Children's Hospital.

In parallel with these developments, the Government had made a decision to rebuild the Children's University Hospital in Temple Street on the nearby campus of the Mater adult hospital. The Children's University Hospital was a very old structure, and its suitability for accommodating children, never mind provide complex medical care for them, was far from adequate. The infrastructure at Temple Street was significantly worse than that at Our Lady's Children's Hospital.

We were therefore facing a situation where there were plans to build a replacement hospital for the Children's University Hospital, while the New Crumlin Hospital Group was now lobbying, with some success, to rebuild Our Lady's Children's Hospital. There was a danger, especially as Ireland was entering an economic boom, that a political decision would be made to proceed with the construction of two new hospitals. This would cast in stone the status quo: a division of complex children's services across different campuses in Dublin, an outcome that would mean we could not provide children with the best possible quality of care.

When I was offered the post of CEO of the HSE I realised that, in addition to progressing changes in the health service in general, this presented me with an incredible opportunity to seek government support for the development of a state-of-the-art children's hospital for Ireland. Within a couple of months of its establishment, the HSE commissioned an independent review of the provision of children's hospital services in Dublin and specialist services for the children of Ireland as a whole. McKinsey & Company were appointed to carry out the independent review. They evaluated best practice internationally for the provision of services for children with complex illnesses.

At the same time, we had to suspend plans for the replacement of the Children's University Hospital, Temple Street. The detailed design for this hospital had been completed and the project was due to go to tender within weeks. It would have made no sense to go ahead with the new Children's University Hospital development without having an independent and expert view of what was required to provide the best possible service for children in Dublin and all over Ireland. Naturally, this decision was heavily criticised by the consultant medical staff and most others at the Children's University Hospital. They had worked hard to get a new facility and, just as their ambition was about to be realised, they were concerned it was slipping away.

On 28 January 2006, in response to the HSE's resolution to suspend a decision on the replacement of their hospital, a letter signed by twenty-one consultants at the Children's University Hospital was published in the *Irish Times*. This stated that the staff at the hospital were 'stunned' by the decision to block the building of their replacement hospital. It stated that the decision to stop the building of the new Temple Street Hospital until the review was completed was sabotage that illustrated 'all that is wrong with our health services'.

A few days later, the Medical Board of Temple Street Hospital issued a statement which was reported in the *Irish Times* on 2 Februrary 2006. The statement included the following: 'We demand that an independent body *fair to all service providers* [my emphasis] be established to explore the matter of tertiary services and that the HSE step back.' I could understand their frustration, which was reflected in their criticism. There was a suspicion, because of my background of working at Our Lady's Children's Hospital, that I was using my position as CEO of the HSE to block the development of their new hospital on the Mater campus.

The response of parents to the decision to set up the McKinsey review was remarkable in its foresight. Their response was reported in the *Irish Times* on 3 January 2006. Linda Dillon, chairperson of the New Crumlin Hospital Group, called for the review of specialist paediatric services to be completed as quickly as possible. She said she hoped there would be no dispute over the campus chosen as the national centre once a decision was made by the review group: 'a dispute would only serve to delay the provision of the best possible service for children.' She went on to say that:

> We have no fixed view as to where the hospital is located, just that it is provided quickly .... It would seem to us to be immoral and wrong for the development of this hospital to be delayed by even one day due to further debates and disputes over its location .... We call on all involved in this process to work together to deliver what is in the best interest of the sickest children of this country without delay. If you put the children first, it is quite clear what needs to be done.

McKinsey & Company proposed that there should only be one children's hospital in Dublin, providing general paediatric services for the children of the greater Dublin area and specialist services for the children of the whole country. This centre, they advised, should be co-located with a major adult hospital and be supported by one or two ambulatory or day-care centres at different locations in the city.

The most critical day in the entire process of developing a new children's hospital was Thursday, 2 February 2006. We had a recommendation based on international best practice to build a single new children's hospital. However, based on past experience it could take twenty years before the funding for such a hospital was provided. In the absence of an immediate commitment by Government to support this proposal, the pressure to proceed with the plans to replace the Children's University Hospital, which we had suspended, would be immense. We had to convince the

Board of the HSE and the Government that this should become a capital expenditure priority for the HSE. This was largely achieved in a remarkable 24-hour period.

On 2 February, I proposed to the Board that the HSE adopt the recommendation in the McKinsey review to build a new children's hospital. The Board endorsed the recommendation. Later that evening, the report was presented to and discussed with the Minister, her advisors and senior civil servants. We sought her immediate support for the project. Despite significant concern expressed by the Department officials about the need for the Department of Health and Children to carry out a full assessment of the effect of this proposal on other potential capital developments, she decided that evening that she would immediately seek government approval for building the new children's hospital. She subsequently obtained this approval.

The commitment by Government of €450 million for the project was a major breakthrough for everybody interested in improving the care provided to sick children in Ireland. The Minister's decision reflected her commitment to the project, which was obvious from the first time I had discussed the HSE's proposal to develop a national centre of excellence for the care of sick children with her. While Department of Health and Children officials were initially surprised by the rapid progression of the project, they also became committed supporters.

The following morning, the proposal that a single children's hospital should be built on an adult hospital campus was presented by us to a broad range of interested parties, including representatives from each of the three existing children's hospitals, at a meeting in a central Dublin hotel. The proposal was warmly welcomed by all, including statements of support from the boards of Our Lady's Children's Hospital and the Children's University Hospital. We were therefore in a situation where not only had the decision to develop a centre of excellence been made, but it was supported by the three children's hospitals and endorsed by Government.

Unfortunately, the good news of widespread agreement was always likely to be short-lived. The next step involved identifying a location for the new hospital. Experience from other countries suggested that this would be fraught with danger. A commentary in the *Irish Times* by the paper's health correspondent Eithne Donnellan, on 4 February 2006, the day after the announcement, was headlined: 'Hospital's Location Will Be Keenly Fought. The Real Battle May only Be Starting.'

Location options were limited by the fact that the McKinsey review had recommended that a new children's hospital should be co-located with an adult hospital. This meant that the hospital could not be built on a greenfield site as there were already more than enough adult hospitals in Dublin for the foreseeable future. The project to identify a location for the new children's hospital, therefore, focused on the five major adult hospitals in Dublin. A group was set up by the HSE to carry out an evaluation of each of these sites. This group comprised engineers and architects from the Office of Public Works and the Department of Health and Children, medical experts from the Department and HSE executives. The group ultimately chose the Mater Hospital campus, a city centre location, which was the site on which the Children's University Hospital, Temple Street was to be rebuilt. Their decision came down to a very close judgement between this campus and that of St James's Hospital, which was on the south side of the river and closer to Our Lady's Children's Hospital. The Mater Hospital was considered to have some significant advantages from a paediatric perspective, as the cardiac surgeons at the Mater provided the paediatric cardiac surgery services at Our Lady's Children's Hospital, and it was also the heart and lung transplant centre. Furthermore, it was relatively close to the adult campus at Beaumont Hospital, which provided kidney transplant and neurosurgery services for children and adults.

Many of those who worked at and used the services at Our Lady's Children's Hospital were extremely unhappy with the decision. Opposition generally centred on claims that the site was too small, there was no green space for children to play in while they were staying in hospital, there was insufficient parking for staff and parents, and there would be no room for expansion.

Those who opposed the decision proposed that the new hospital be built on a greenfield campus, ideally on a ring road around Dublin. This suggestion was contrary to the proposals of the McKinsey review, which stated, based on international best practice, that the hospital should be built on an adult hospital campus. Furthermore, the decision to build a new children's hospital had been followed by a proposal from Our Lady's Children's Hospital that a maternity hospital should be built on the same campus in order to provide adequate care for newborn babies known to be at high risk prior to their birth. This was a very sensible proposal, but also made it imperative that the hospital should be co-located with an adult hospital, as there could be no justification for building a maternity hospital on a site separate to an adult hospital. Any such decision would be ignoring the increased risks that this created for women.

The New Crumlin Hospital Group, representing parents of children who used the services at Our Lady's Children's Hospital, had its own international expert review the site selected, and subsequently gave the plan to build the hospital on the Mater campus its full support. The group formed a view that if an external review, which included significant international expertise, recommended a single children's hospital, then that was what should be built. Furthermore, it accepted the view, based on the international evidence, that the new hospital should be co-located with an adult hospital.

Once the New Crumlin Hospital Group declared its support for building the new hospital on the Mater campus there was an attempt by some to undermine the group's credibility. This was most unfortunate; it was a low point. These parents had invested significant effort and expertise over a number of years in pursuing a new hospital for children. I believe they are the people who did most to deliver a new children's hospital. If the New Crumlin Hospital Group had not commissioned the Pollock Report to justify the replacement of Our Lady's Children's Hospital it would have been impossible to convince the Department of Health and Children and the political system that an international review of the entire children's hospital system was required, rather than simply proceeding to replace the Children's University Hospital, Temple Street. The Pollock Report was highly effective because the Government had to accept that it was commissioned by parents whose only interest was the care of their children and it could not be portrayed otherwise. As a result of the Pollock Report, we at the HSE were able to justify carrying out the McKinsey review because we could demonstrate to Government that, after spending €200 to €300 million on rebuilding the Children's University Hospital, Temple Street, there would still be a requirement to spend another €350 to €400 million at Crumlin, and we would end up with the status quo rather than the best outcome for children.

The campaign to stop the development of the new Children's Hospital of Ireland on the Mater Hospital campus was in many respects very successful. It created a sense of doubt in the minds of the public and fuelled a conspiracy theory that there was political interference, based on the fact that the Mater campus was in the constituency of the then Taoiseach, Bertie Ahern. There were reports of clandestine meetings between the Taoiseach and me. I can state that he never raised the question of the location of the new Children's Hospital of Ireland with me. In contrast, on a number of occasions in Government Buildings he asked me about the timelines for developing the new adult hospital, which the HSE was funding, on the Mater campus. Furthermore, I had no input into the choosing of the site by the committee established to make this decision.

In an attempt to reassure the various interest groups in the three children's hospitals, the HSE arranged for a panel of international experts to visit Ireland to review the campus and the McKinsey recommendation on a single hospital, and to discuss the concerns expressed by different stakeholders. Leaders from the world of paediatrics, paediatric surgery, hospital planning and nursing from Philadelphia, New York, Toronto and Manchester were engaged in this process. Five of them travelled to Dublin in 2007 to visit the campus and engage directly with groups from the individual children's hospitals and with representatives of parents' groups and other members of the public. The international group fully supported the recommendations of the McKinsey review to develop a single children's hospital. Furthermore, having visited the campus and reviewed the work of the project team that choose the site, all five of them, including an architect of international renown in hospital design, endorsed the decision on the location.

Some of the meetings between the experts and groups from the individual children's hospitals were very robust. The international visitors were challenged very forcefully and, indeed, directly accused of not having an adequate understanding of the Irish healthcare system. It was interesting that the members of the international group were individually able to give examples of having faced the very same challenges in their own or other centres across the world and having had the same fears outlined to them in relation to the amalgamation of children's services elsewhere.

A most telling experience during this process was the way groups from the individual children's hospitals described their reasons for adopting specific positions on the planned hospital site. The paediatric experts from the Children's University Hospital, Temple St, which is beside the site chosen for the new hospital, were in unanimous agreement that this was an ideal plan to provide the best possible specialist care for Irish children.

They were followed by the group from Our Lady's Children's Hospital, Crumlin, who described how this proposed plan for Ireland could never achieve the level of excellence required, based on their experience, and that the plan was incapable of providing optimal care for children. The international experts were bemused at the remarkable unanimity on each side, while each took totally opposite views as to what was in the best interests of children. Interestingly, the response from others, who had no affiliation with any of the institutions who participated in this engagement, was that we had to get on with it.

The stakeholder engagement with international experts did not necessarily change any minds that were fixed, but it did reassure the Irish political system and the Department of Health and Children that the HSE decision was the right decision. It was another small step forward in the process of change.

Recanting this story could create the impression that Our Lady's Children's Hospital, Crumlin was intentionally opposing the decision to further their own interests. This would be unfair. In fact, as noted earlier, the Children's University Hospital, Temple Street had responded in a similar way when they were understandably frustrated by the decision of the HSE to stop the building of their new hospital in late 2005, until the McKinsey review was complete. The people in Our Lady's Children's Hospital were right that the site was not ideal in every way. Unfortunately, there is, of course, no ideal site in a city for a new hospital like this.

This type of response was also not unique to Dublin or to Ireland, and similar heated debates had taken place or were underway in other cities across the world, resulting in delays in reconfiguring the children's services for many of the same reasons. Cities like Manchester and Brisbane were or had been in identical positions, proposing the amalgamation of three children's units into one new hospital to serve their catchment areas. In both cities, acrimonious debates stalled the development for several years, especially in Manchester where twenty years were lost because of disagreements among clinicians in the different hospitals before the new children's hospital was built.

The entire process of developing the new children's hospital is yet another example of change for the better which caused significant criticism of the HSE over a number of years. This again confirms that organisations sticking to an evidenced-based approach to doing the right thing in healthcare are unlikely to have popular approval. There is, of course, no ideal site in a city for a new hospital like this.

The process provided significant insights from the Department of Health and Children's perspective. They had traditionally operated on the basis that decisions to implement change were only taken when consensus was achieved with all the different interests on the way forward. You cannot blame the Department for this approach to decision making. They had little choice, being directly responsible to the Government of the day, which in turn came under immense pressure from backbench politicians opposed to the proposed changes if they affected their local areas.

In this case, the political system, the Department, the public and other stakeholders had seen the HSE carry out an expert review of a service, come forward with a proposal for a change in the service based on best international practice, develop a plan to implement this change and proceed to implement it following further international validation. This process continued, despite significant lobbying in the media by groups who were unhappy about the change. It should be acknowledged that, as a result of this transparent process, the HSE received committed support from the Minister for Health and Children and her government colleagues for the building of the hospital. Without her and the Government's support in the face of huge media pressure, and also the support of the civil servants in the Department of Health and Children, it would have been very difficult to keep advancing the project.

This support has persisted with the new Government, which came into office in March 2011. Because of the significant debate that had taken place, it was not surprising that the new Minister for Health, Dr James Reilly, wanted to be reassured of the transparency of the process by asking a further group of experts from the US, Australia and the UK to review the decision. This international group not only strongly endorsed the decision to build the new hospital at the Mater campus, but stressed the importance of doing so immediately.

CHAPTER 9

Primary Care Teams: An Essential Building Block of Integrated Care

The term 'integrated care' can mean different things to different people. To understand what integrated care means you should put yourself in the place of an individual living in the community who has many healthcare needs – such as Tom (see Chapter 1) – and decide how you would want your care managed in that situation. Once you place yourself in Tom's shoes, it becomes relatively easy to outline how services should be organised to optimally care for him. As mentioned in Chapter 1, the type of service that we would all want for ourselves and our families is that where most of our care is provided to us in our local communities. This care should be provided by teams of professionals who have a care plan for us and everyone knows what the others are doing.

In 2001, the Department of Health and Children developed a plan for primary care called the Primary Care Strategy. It proposed the formation of primary care teams in centres across the country. It was seen as a way of improving the care provided at a community level. While it did not provide a wider vision of integrated care, in terms of moving care from hospitals to the community and reconfiguring hospital services, the Primary Care Strategy was nevertheless very important. Initially, the Government committed investment to develop ten pilot primary care teams across the country. Unfortunately little else was done over subsequent years and most would accept that the initiative had petered out by the time the HSE was established.

In 2006, as we developed the HSE transformation programme, it was clear that if we were committed to improving the experience of those who used our services the development of primary care teams was essential. While media commentators saw the building of the primary care centres as the major challenge and, indeed, the measure of success in developing primary care teams, building the infrastructure, while slow, is the easy bit. The really difficult and slow part of developing primary care teams was selling the vision for integrated care to the staff of the HSE, especially those who worked in community-based services, and getting them to agree to work in a totally different way than before. We had thousands of public health nurses, physiotherapists, dieticians, social workers and others up and down the country, all of whom were used to providing services to their communities as individual professional groups. Furthermore, each of these groups had their own managerial structure or hierarchy, and redesigning the system to create multidisciplinary teams was going to reduce the number of senior positions available to each professional group.

Getting Support from Professionals

The challenge for the HSE was to convince each professional group in different parts of the country that integrated multidisciplinary teams could provide much better care for their patients. The story of Tom's experience was an opportunity to make the potential gains of establishing primary care teams tangible, both from the perspective of care providers and those who lived in communities across the country. As teams were formed, we depended on members of these teams in turn communicating the message to others in their profession.

We also had to convince communities of the importance of developing an integrated approach to providing healthcare, not only to obtain support for the development of primary care teams but to get people to understand that building further hospitals, such as the proposed 3,000 beds, was not necessarily in their best interests. If the 3,000-bed development proposed by Government and opposition parties had proceeded, we would not have the human resources to begin developing primary care teams in the community. More and more, healthcare professionals would be tied up in the expanding hospital system. More importantly, giving out such a mixed message would have made it impossible to convince healthcare professionals that we were committed to building an integrated model of care focused on as many services as possible being provided in the community.

As with all change programmes, success was dependent on individual leaders. A dynamic director of public health nursing, or a lead social worker or physiotherapist, can be a powerful catalyst for change. In some community areas we were fortunate to have such leaders in a number of different disciplines, which provided a great opportunity to bring about rapid change in that particular location.

There was one group of professionals who were essential to the development of primary care teams and without whose commitment we could never make significant progress. These were the GPs. GPs in Ireland, as in many other countries, are self-employed, although significantly funded by the State for the services they provide to many of their patients. They are understandably protective of their independence as self-employed individuals and many of them were sceptical about any involvement with the HSE, which they saw as a State agency trying to take control of their practices.

Some GPs justified their hesitation to embrace the primary care team model on the basis that they already provided an excellent service through their existing structures. They compared themselves to services in other countries such as the UK and pointed out that, in Ireland, a GP was available immediately for patients on the day care was requested, without any need to wait. It was difficult to argue with this, as there was no doubt that the existing general practice system provided excellent access for patients. As a result, there was justifiably a high level of satisfaction among their patients with the care they provided.

It can be, therefore, difficult for GPs to accept that change is required. To do so, you have to accept that the overall system of care is not working or at least is underperforming and you, despite the excellence of your own individual practice, are part of this underperforming system. There is a responsibility on all of us healthcare professionals to accept the need to change the way we do things in order to improve the overall service for patients. This is especially important for GPs, as they are often the most likely leaders in developing primary care teams.

While GPs were individually providing an excellent service for their patients, there were problems with the provision of healthcare services in the community. For example, a GP often had little or no access to physiotherapy services for a patient with back pain. Having seen a patient with alcohol addiction the GP would have to refer him or her to a different service. When faced with a patient with an acute symptom like chest pain a GP had no immediate access to a senior clinical decision maker, or diagnostic tests in hospital. While GPs were providing the best possible service that could be expected under the existing system, by forming primary care teams they could ensure that services were reorganised in a way that would deliver integrated community-based services for their patients.

GPs working in rural environments often take responsibility for improving the quality of the overall healthcare service that is provided in their community. They try to provide a more comprehensive range of services for their patients because they may be a significant distance from the nearest hospital. Public health nursing may be the only service in the area. Patients may have to travel some distance for community-based services such as speech and language therapy, occupational therapy or physiotherapy. GPs are acutely aware of the deficits that exist in community-based services in their area, irrespective of the excellent care they themselves provide.

GPs in rural areas are, therefore, often positive about engaging with the development of primary care teams, because they can identify the benefits that will flow from such teams. They can see that having physiotherapy or occupational therapy provided on set days for their patients, having an addiction counsellor or mental health nurse visit their practice on a particular day, or having planned access to speech and language therapy can greatly enhance services in their community. In addition, by the very nature of the environment they live and work in, rural GPs tend to be leaders in their communities, not only in healthcare but at a broader level. This leadership role makes them ideal for developing and leading primary care teams and also allows them to identify with the wider impact that such teams can have in their community.

By contrast, GPs working in urban environments often have a different type of practice. Many of the required services, such as physiotherapy or social work or addiction counselling, are provided in their city or town but through completely separate professional systems. In an urban environment GPs focus on the service they provide themselves, and any deficits in the provision of other professional services are not their responsibility.

This may be understandable, but it is difficult to justify the continuation of a system where the overall service is of a poorer quality because individual professional silos are maintained.

In the past, it has been reported that GPs and public health nurses working in large urban centres often did not have each other's mobile phone number. It is even less likely that GPs and other community service providers, such as therapists, had any significant interaction. In contrast, the GPs, public health nurses, physiotherapist, occupational therapist, home help providers and others working in the primary care team on Achill Island and in Mulranny in rural Co. Mayo are all in regular contact with each other as they care for people in their community. When you visit them, their enthusiasm as a team to improve their services and their commitment to supporting each other in providing care is palpable.

In larger cities such as Dublin, GPs who work in deprived areas often appear to be more aligned with the views of their rural colleagues. They are aware of the positive effects that a team-based approach can have on the quality of services that their patients can access. Again, they are often the first point of contact not just for health, but for social care problems for people in these deprived communities. GPs can best respond to these problems if they work in a multidisciplinary primary care team structure. The leadership shown by many of the GPs who have developed primary care teams in these environments has been inspirational.

Developing Primary Care Teams

Primary care teams were initially developed based on the level of interest expressed by individual GPs and various professional leaders in community services. It became clear to us that this approach was going to lead to a very uneven distribution of teams across the country and marked inconsistencies in how teams were established and led. The appointment of Ms Laverne McGuinness as head of our Primary, Community and Continuing Care (PCCC) services in 2007 was a major step forward, as she had the capacity to formally organise the large-scale programmes of change that were required to support these developments. She appointed a senior manager, Mr Brian Murphy, with responsibility for developing primary care teams across the country. They in turn appointed a group of team development officers who worked as team builders with GPs and with local community-based professionals to establish individual primary care teams. The role of the team development officer was of vital importance.

The greatest challenge for the team development officers continued to be convincing GPs to join teams. They also had to convince the healthcare professionals, such as public health nurses, therapists and others, to join the teams and work in a manner that was very different to before. Creating a successful interface between HSE-employed nurses, therapists and other community-based workers, and independently managed GP services was and still is a considerable challenge.

Team development officers had to consider themselves as pioneers driving a seismic change in how healthcare was provided in Ireland, and had to be passionate about the need for change so that we could improve care for people in local communities. The success of primary care team development in specific areas is to a large extent due to the remarkable leadership and enthusiasm shown by the team development officers in those areas. Their passion for improving care was central to their success.

A standardised approach was established to setting up primary care teams and formalising their work practices. This was not a rigid structure in terms of the types of professionals involved in a team, as this would vary from team to team. In some areas with largely elderly populations physiotherapy and occupational therapy might be a priority, whereas in others with a young community or a deprived community social workers might be a priority.

Incentivising GPs to Join Teams

The major breakthrough in getting GPs to join primary care teams in large numbers did not come from me or any of our clinicians or team development officers. It came from a civil engineer, Mr Brian Gilroy, who had joined the HSE as head of the Estates Directorate. Brian identified early on that if we had to convince individual general practices across the country one by one to join teams we could never hope to deliver a comprehensive primary care structure. He could see that the fear of losing their independence was a big stumbling block for GPs. He saw an opportunity to incentivise GPs to become a central part of developing primary care teams by giving them ownership of the new infrastructure required to house the teams.

In essence, he developed a type of public–private partnership approach to developing primary care centres. The HSE identified approximately 200 locations across Ireland where we wanted to build primary care centres, and these 200 centres would accommodate just over 500 teams. The reason for the difference in numbers is that in larger towns and cities three to four primary care teams could operate out of one centre because of the density of population. Each team would care for a population of approximately 10,000 people, and there would be 4–5 GPs on the team.

Having identified the locations for the primary care centres, the composition of these teams, which would be different in different locations, was then planned. A standardised approach was taken to the amount and type of space needed for each professional, e.g. a physiotherapist or a social worker. This allowed the HSE to accurately outline how much space it required for the multidisciplinary team in each centre.

A tendering process was established and expressions of interest were requested from groups interested in building any of the primary care centres. The HSE would commit to leasing the space it required for its community-based professionals, such as public health nurses, physiotherapists and social workers, for twenty years. This created a blue chip tenant for the developer. A competitive market was thereby created as this was a very attractive investment opportunity, especially since Ireland was in the middle of a real estate boom at the time.

The central requirement for each primary care centre was that, regardless of who the developer was, they had to have the required number of GPs contracted to work in the centre. Furthermore, the GPs had to agree to work within the primary care team structure and if they withdrew from the team structure the lease was no longer valid.

This approach was dependent on GPs joining and continuing to remain as part of the team. GPs, therefore, were in a powerful position to develop the centres themselves or at least to become vital partners with developers in creating the centres. The approach was very successful. We had applications, often from several groups, for practically every centre that was proposed across the country. This meant that, overnight, we had buy-in from groups of GPs across the country to develop the primary care teams.

Political Support

The success of this programme also depended on government acceptance that the public–private partnership approach could be used to develop primary care teams. The advantages of a public–private partnership approach are much greater than just getting buy-in for primary care teams from GPs. It also means that the infrastructure is developed through the private sector, which is a quicker delivery model. Furthermore, maintenance of the centres is the responsibility of the developers. The downside of this approach is the fact that there is an ongoing annual charge against the HSE budget allocation to pay for the primary care centres because of the leases. Nevertheless, the overall expenditure from a revenue perspective would reach a maximum of €80 million a year in an organisation with a budget of €13 billion per year. While the long-term revenue commitment was a source of concern for some individuals, both within the Department of Health and Children and within the HSE Board, primary care team development was such an important building block for the entire transformation programme that people committed to it.

The commitment by the political system to support this approach was based on a growing acceptance among politicians that the entire concept of primary care team development was positive from their communities' perspective. While they could not say so in public, politicians began to realise that primary care teams were in many respects more important than their local hospital. For example, in 2006 I met with politicians from Co. Roscommon, where the hospital continued to operate in Roscommon Town, providing medical and surgical services but with little or no overnight or weekend surgical activity. The politicians were focused on maintaining this hospital as a going concern. A year later, when I met the same politicians, their focus had changed significantly. While still expressing concern about the hospital, they now wanted to clarify where their local primary care centres were going to be built because they had seen two primary care teams established and could see that the teams were going to greatly improve the services available to their communities. Convincing politicians of the advantages of establishing primary care centres over investing in hospitals is the key to moving this programme along. As this book goes to print there is much local concern and political fallout about the discontinuation of emergency services in Roscommon Hospital. However, at the same time, a wonderful new purpose-built primary care centre has opened in the town. This is how local healthcare provision must proceed if we are to ensure the best possible care for the whole population.

Progress to Date

We reached a point where criticism of our plan to develop primary care teams, rather than build 3,000 hospital beds, moved from insisting that primary care teams were illusionary to challenging the HSE as to why the process was not happening more quickly. Commentators, including clinicians who for years had advocated more hospital capacity, were now proclaiming that more beds were not the solution, but rather that we needed to build up our community-based services and change the way our hospitals provided care. This indicated that we were making significant progress and were now getting buy-in across the public, political and healthcare stakeholders. The reconfiguration of health services was now moving in the right direction.

The infrastructure for the early centres was of an extremely high quality, and this was a further incentive for professionals to join teams. Furthermore, from a performance perspective, waiting lists in areas like physiotherapy and occupational therapy decreased dramatically or disappeared when professionals moved to work in a multidisciplinary team environment. Some of this related to improved productivity on the part of professionals, but it also presumably related to referrals becoming more appropriate when professionals operate in a team-based environment.

One of the most positive aspects of the development of primary care teams was the improved job satisfaction among healthcare professionals. As I visited teams across the country, from Letterkenny to Cork, Abbeyleix to Ringsend, Achill Island to Pearse Street and Ballymun in Dublin, GPs, therapists and other healthcare professionals working in primary care teams constantly spoke of the fact that they could achieve so much more by working in teams. More importantly, they felt that their interaction with each other was professionally stimulating and led to a more enjoyable work environment.

While GPs were always a central part of their communities, most other health professionals were not. In a primary care team structure, all professionals and carers feel relevant to their community and have a pride in what they can achieve in improving the quality of care provided to people in their area. I was inspired by a visit to the Abbeyleix primary care team. A young physiotherapist described how she provided courses at night in the local community hall, informing older people how to care for their backs by avoiding positions that would damage their backs and carrying out exercises to strengthen their back muscles. This was unpaid work. She did it because she felt responsible as the local physiotherapist for this population. She described her satisfaction in being so relevant to her community and being able to contribute in this way.

Ultimately, one of the most important interfaces for primary care teams is with their own community. Primary care teams provide a focal point where all State-provided and voluntary services can interact. As part of the structured national approach to developing primary care teams, a formal interactive process with community groups in each area was established. The existence of the primary care teams allows community groups such as those working with elderly people or the poor in an area to engage directly with both health and social care services on the team. Voluntary community groups can often identify those who are isolated or lonely or, indeed, abused in their communities and can have these situations managed through the primary care structure. Similarly, it allows primary care team professionals to identify and engage with those in community groups who can provide support for patients they are treating within a community environment.

The primary care team structure can genuinely empower communities to participate in the development of health, mental health and personal social services in their area. The evolution of this interaction over the next ten to fifteen years will, I believe, be the most exciting part of the development of integrated care.

The criticism that centres have not been built more quickly is, of course, understandable. Everyone now wants these structures in place in their communities. The economic downturn has affected the speed of delivery of centres, because financing for developments, even with a committed blue chip tenant, has become much more difficult. By the end of 2011, over 50 of the 200 planned centres will have been completed or are under construction. While this means the building of all centres will still take several years to complete, the more fundamental process of team building among GPs and other community health and social care professionals is now well advanced: 377 (72 per cent) of the 520 planned primary care teams have been initiated. The development of the teams varies from those in the early stages to those that are fully functioning in their communities. Over the next ten years, the balance of power in healthcare will gradually move from hospitals to these community-based teams, much to the benefit of people who use health and social care services. There is no light switch to make this happen. It is, for everybody who works in healthcare, as much a cultural change as a structural change, but the road is marked out and the journey is well underway.

Chapter 10

A New Consultant Contract

The work practices of consultants are critical in determining how effectively a hospital delivers services. Their practices are central in determining when patients are seen, how many are seen each day and how patients are prioritised in terms of access to care. Consultants also determine what tests and procedures patients require. Therefore, they not only determine the ease of access to services, but also, to a large extent, the demand for many services provided by the hospital. As a result, they have a significant impact on the costs associated with the provision of healthcare. The contractual relationship between the health service and consultants is therefore of great importance. Changes in their practices were essential if an integrated healthcare service was to function optimally.

In 2005, almost all consultants in Ireland had one of two contracts: a Category 1 or a Category 2 contract. Category 1 contract holders were, in addition to their commitment to public patients, allowed to conduct private practice within the public hospital. While they could not practice in any other hospital, the amount of private practice carried out in the public hospital was not restricted. Category 2 contract holders provided services for patients in public hospitals, but they also had an unrestricted right to provide services in any private hospitals they chose to work in. Despite the fact that they were full-time public service employees, there was no restriction on the amount of private practice they could engage in, in either public or private hospitals.

With such a system, there is a significant risk of creating a perverse incentive for consultants. This is because longer waiting lists in the public health service generate a significant increase in work for the same practitioners in the private health service. Patients who are facing long waiting lists will often choose to access the same consultants' services through the private system. In 2005, there was no other developed country where such a system existed, apart from Australia.

The Category 2 contract created further problems, as consultants with this contract were often committed to managing patients on at least one other hospital site in the private sector. Consultants working across multiple sites as private practitioners in addition to their public work had to struggle with developing a team-based approach to working. There was also the difficulty of looking after very ill patients in different hospitals, sometimes a significant distance apart. In contrast, consultants who held Category 1 contracts were usually committed to a single hospital, thereby ensuring their presence on-site on a consistent basis. They were available to all of the patients in the hospital, public or private, at any time.

There were a number of other fundamental problems with the existing contracts: they provided for no hierarchical structure and each consultant essentially operated as an individual practitioner who, to a large extent, was totally responsible for his or her own performance. There was no measurement of consultant activity, either comparing private to public activity or, indeed, comparing the overall activity of one consultant with another, and there was little accountability for attendance.

The Government and the Board of the HSE initially decided that a new contract would confine consultants to treating public patients only. They would not be allowed to bill for any service provided to patients with private insurance in public hospitals. This would certainly have removed the potential perverse incentive that existed within the system. However, I was concerned that such an approach would not necessarily improve performance from a public patient's perspective, as consultants paid through a public-only contract might simply limit their activity. Consultants are in a position to choose to do this, based on their independence as clinical decision makers. I, therefore, took a different view, which was that we could use private activity and potential earnings from private patients to incentivise consultants to improve services for public patients. In Ireland, we are always going to have emergency patients with private insurance admitted to our public hospitals. It seemed reasonable that we should try to use this source of income to incentivise consultants to improve the overall delivery of service.

I agreed that we had to negotiate a contract that restricted consultants to working in the public hospital system only. However, within this environment, I wanted to allow consultants to provide care for private patients up to a total of 20 per cent of their activity. This ultimately was referred to as the 80/20 Rule. There were a number of reasons for holding this view. The private income associated with 20 per cent of patients could incentivise increased activity overall. If a consultant wished to increase their income, it was going to be in their interest to increase their public activity so that the amount of private activity could increase. An additional benefit was that the introduction of an 80/20 approach would make it essential for consultants to document their activity accurately. This would be a major bonus to the service, as accurate documentation, not only of the number of patients seen but the level of complexity of the patients treated, is often difficult to obtain because consultants must take time to use internationally validated coding systems to document accurately their clinical activity with patients. Linking their private insurance remuneration to their overall activity would incentivise consultants to document their work in this manner. This level of detailed information is of immense benefit to hospitals and the wider healthcare service in terms of planning services and understanding financial performance.

The Department of Health and Children and the Board of the HSE were initially opposed to this proposal. There was a lot of frustration that consultants in some specialties appeared to be able to devote a huge amount of time to private practice under the old contracts. There were often long waiting lists for public patients for access to services, while the same consultant's private patients had immediate access to the same public hospital, which was fully funded by the taxpayer. Any proposal that would allow private practice to continue was therefore considered to have significant risks.

There was also much scepticism that we could develop an accurate measurement system through which consultants could be held to account in terms of the 80/20 approach. However, over a period of time, a team in the HSE, under the leadership of Ms Maureen Lynott, was able to develop a measurement system.

A major concern of mine about introducing a contract that did not allow any private practice was that existing consultants who held Category 1 and 2 contracts would refuse to sign a new contract, and would just continue with their old contracts. This would have had a very significant impact on the HSE's transformation programme, as the new contract was aimed at introducing changes that were central to driving the programme to deliver a better quality health service. These included the development of a hierarchical structure, with consultants reporting to clinical directors; the introduction of a weekly schedule with a specific detailed outline of daily duties; new disciplinary procedures which were greatly simplified in comparison to the old contracts; and an extended working day. If the majority of consultants remained on the old contract, which was their right, moving to a team-based approach with a clinical director leading the changes in practice was going to be impossible. Eventually, after many long meetings, we were able to convince the Board of the HSE and the Secretary General of the Department of Health and Children that the 80/20 approach had significant advantages and that it was likely that many more consultants would move to such a new contract.

The proposal to introduce a contract that would allow consultants to work in public hospitals only was well flagged in advance of the opening of negotiations with the consultants and their representative organisations. The private hospitals expressed concerns that they would not be able to recruit consultants of adequate standing under such circumstances. They had, for many years, benefited from a situation where highly trained Irish doctors, often returning from major international centres to work in the Irish public hospitals, were also allowed to work for private hospitals. This situation had become so established that it was perceived as being unreasonable when the HSE proposed that people employed by public hospitals could only work in public hospitals.

The private hospitals initiated a lobbying campaign aimed at the Government, the Department of Health and Children, and the HSE to try to have this decision reversed. This lobbying campaign gathered significant support. It was essential, however, that we did not agree to any change in our approach. As noted above, the potential perverse incentive that existed for consultants in terms of their performance in the public sector under such conditions was obvious. In years to come, it will be very difficult for people looking back at this to understand the rationale that justified any objection to this approach to a new contract. However, all practices, no matter how irrational, will, if continued, ultimately become identified as acceptable in a system.

Co-Location of Private Hospitals with Public Hospitals

The Government had decided by 2005 to initiate a scheme that would provide tax incentives for private healthcare operators to build private hospitals on sites adjacent to public hospitals. This plan was introduced because of the perceived need, at the time, for a significant increase in the number of beds required by the healthcare system. The Government's rationale for the proposed approach was straightforward. It would facilitate privately insured emergency patients, who were being admitted to public hospitals, to be admitted instead to a co-located private hospital. This would free up capacity within the public hospital system and would reduce costs for the public hospitals by reducing the amount of emergency care they had to provide. It would also dramatically increase costs for the private healthcare system.

I had a fundamental concern about the co-located hospital project. My concern was that consultants who worked in the public hospital were to be allowed to provide services in the co-located private hospital. An even greater concern was the fact that the Government was asking the HSE to agree that the new consultant contract would allow such consultants to provide services in the co-located private hospital without any measurement of this activity. It was proposed that such activity should be of no interest to the State once a consultant had already fulfilled his or her full weekly contractual commitment in the public hospital. From my perspective, this approach would significantly undermine our capacity to manage the public hospital system.

The HSE's goal of improving the performance of the hospitals was dependent on introducing a culture of performance measurement and management, driving increased effectiveness in terms of the provision of services. If co-located private hospitals were built, there was going to be a considerable incentive for consultants working in the public hospitals to underperform, knowing that underperformance would significantly increase their annual incomes because it would increase the work available for them in the co-located private hospitals.

This, for me, was a fundamental issue and I could not continue to manage the public health service in a situation where this approach was implemented. The Board of the HSE and the Department of Health and Children were, however, very supportive of this approach to developing co-located hospitals. In some respects it is understandable that they might hold this view, as in other businesses outside of medical care this approach might seem logical. However, in a clinical environment, where the provider, i.e. the consultant, determines both the pace at which services will be provided and often the amount of service that is provided, the situation is very different.

This issue led to a significant disagreement between a group comprising the Minister, the Secretary General of the Department of Health and Children, and the Chairman of the Board on the one hand, and me on the other. I had to document for them my concern that a contract which allowed consultants unrestricted access to private practice in co-located private hospitals would essentially undermine our public hospital system.

The 80/20 approach to managing private activity provided a solution to this problem. The HSE proposed that the 80/20 Rule would apply to all activity on the site, including the co-located private hospital. There would be a contractual relationship between the public and private hospital whereby all activity data would be shared between the private hospital and the public hospital. This would mean that the HSE could ensure that consultants did not work beyond their agreed 20 per cent of overall activity in terms of the provision of care to privately insured patients.

Negotiating the New Consultant Contract

Having finally reached agreement on the HSE side that a new contract would be based on consultants working only in public hospitals, but that they would be allowed up to 20 per cent private practice, we were in a position to initiate negotiations on the development of a new contract with the consultant representative bodies: the Irish Hospital Consultants Association (IHCA) and the Irish Medical Organisation (IMO). The IHCA negotiation team was led by their Chief Executive, Mr Finbarr Fitzpatrick, whereas the IMO were led by their Head of Industrial Relations, Mr

Fintan Hourihan. The IHCA represented the majority of consultants. We were proposing two contracts: (i) a public-only contract for consultants who did not wish to have any private practice, and (ii) a contract that would allow 80 per cent public and 20 per cent private activity.

The negotiations on the new consultant contract, between teams representing the IHCA and IMO and negotiators from the HSE and the Department, went on for several weeks. Eventually it was decided that Michael Scanlan, the Secretary General at the Department, and I should join the discussions in an effort to reach agreement on some of the major issues involved. Among the many issues of contention, the most significant were the measurement and control of the amount of private practice that could be carried out and a consultant's right to work in private hospitals.

Another notable issue was the introduction of clinical directors to whom consultants would report. The representative bodies held the view that consultants did not work optimally in a team environment, and that it was essential that each consultant had absolute protection of their right to practice as an individual and independence in decision making. This was a surprising approach, considering that consultants in some of the world's most famous hospitals have for decades practised through hierarchical and team-based structures. The two organisations also had concerns about the introduction of new disciplinary procedures.

Michael Scanlan and I were involved in negotiations with the two representative bodies over an almost continuous 48-hour timeframe. From an early stage, it was obvious that there was a constructive approach among the IHCA negotiating team to agreeing a contract that would be consistent with the transformation programme for the health services. Some of their consultant negotiators had a comprehensive understanding of and commitment to the transformation programme and were able to communicate this to their colleagues. I believe that the IMO representatives were also committed to change but, because the IMO is the representative body for other groups, including junior hospital doctors, public health doctors and GPs, it may have been much more difficult for them to commit to negotiating a very different approach to how doctors would provide services in the future. In any event, the IMO negotiating team, following a brief visit from the chief executive of the organisation, decided to walk out of the negotiations for reasons that were not clear to those of us on the HSE side of the table, or I suspect to the IHCA.

Following the walkout, which took place in the middle of the night, we had concerns that the IHCA team would also leave because of the risk they might be portrayed as not maintaining a hard enough line in the negotiations. Remarkable leadership was shown on that night by Finbarr Fitzpatrick, the chief executive of the IHCA, who, following discussions with his team, agreed to continue with the negotiations. Over the subsequent twenty-four hours, we were able to agree the outline for a new contract for consultants which would be very different to the contract it was to replace.

One of the major changes in the new contract was the acceptance of an 80/20 approach to public/private practice for new consultant appointments. Perhaps even more importantly, consultants who signed this contract would in the future work in public hospitals only. This was referred to as a Category B contract. In order to incentivise existing consultants to sign the new contract, the HSE accepted that they would be allowed to have up to 30 per cent of their practice as private practice, i.e. a 70/30 split. A second form of contract, referred to as a Category A contract, would be a public-only contract where consultants could not charge private patients or conduct any private practice.

A major stumbling block in the negotiations was the IHCA's insistence on the continuation of a form of contract that would allow consultants to work in private hospitals, equivalent to the old Category 2 contract. This, for reasons outlined above, was a line in the sand for those of us negotiating on the HSE side. The issue proved intractable in the negotiations as it was obviously of great importance to the consultants to maintain this remarkable arrangement from the past. Eventually it was agreed that we would include a Category C contract, which would allow consultants to work in a private hospital as well as in public hospitals. However, we agreed to this only on the basis that the fundamental criterion for the decision to issue such a contract was that it would serve the best interests of the public. A committee would be established, with a majority of the committee representing the public interest, to determine when such a contract could be issued. This, in essence, was confirming that such a contract could only be put in place under exceptional circumstances.

A very significant change in the new contract was the agreement to introduce clinical directors to whom consultants would report in a hierarchical structure. There was agreement to introduce for each consultant a specific schedule of activities for each day of the week, which could be audited as required to ensure adequate performance. This contrasted with the old contract where attendance was almost impossible to monitor. The introduction of an extended day over which consultants could be asked to work, from 8.00 a.m. to 8.00 p.m., was agreed. Finally, there was agreement on a more straightforward approach to dealing with disciplinary procedures.

There remained a concern that consultants with very large private practices would not sign up to the new contract because it would result in significant diminution of their existing income from private practice. About 20 per cent of consultants had existing Category 2 contracts, which allowed them to practise in private hospitals, many of whom practised surgery and interventional medical specialities such as cardiology or gastroenterology. To ensure that these consultants joined the hierarchical structure and the team-based approach an exception was made that would allow these existing Category 2 consultants to sign a specific contract, referred to as a B-Star contract. This allowed them to continue to work in private hospitals for the duration of their professional careers, but they would sign up to all of the other changes in the new contractual agreement.

Ultimately, 90 per cent of consultants signed the new consultant contract. This could not have been achieved if the Government and the HSE had continued to insist on a public-only contract as the only option.

The challenge, then, for the HSE was the implementation of the new contract on the ground, including adherence to the 80/20 rule on access to private practice. The contract allowed for the repayment of funds to a research and education fund within the hospital by consultants who operated outside of their contracted 80/20 or 70/30 arrangement. We were able to achieve agreement relatively quickly with the consultant bodies in terms of the specific measurement arrangements for activity, which would take account of the complexity of the patients seen as well as the number of patients.

The IMO quickly re-entered talks with the HSE following agreement being achieved with the IHCA. They ultimately agreed to the same contractual arrangements. Their decision to walk out of the negotiations was, I believe, seen by many as ill-judged and probably represented a bygone era in terms of an approach to negotiations between consultants and healthcare management. I believe that they misjudged the commitment of many consultants across the country to the transformation programme and their genuine desire to see significant change in the way we provided services.

The new consultant contract is central to changing the way we provide healthcare services to the public in Ireland over the next twenty years. It had immediate benefits, for example the introduction of a hierarchical model with clinical directors driving change. However, the full impact of the contractual change will not be seen for a number of years because of the gradual process of increasing the number of consultants who are fully committed to the public hospital system, as consultants who held the old Category 2 and now a B-Star contract retire. We will arrive at a point where almost all consultants working in Irish public hospitals are contractually bound to the public hospital. This will also lead to a situation where other consultants will work only in the private hospital system. These changes will, I believe, result in a much more equitable approach to the provision of health services from the public's perspective.

Chapter 11

Clinical Leadership

Perhaps the biggest error made in managing the Irish health service over several decades was the virtual exclusion of practising clinicians, including doctors, nurses and others, from any significant role in managing the service. Prior to the establishment of the health board structure in the 1970s, health services were provided through the local government system, which is based on county boundaries. Under that system, clinical leadership took the form of a county surgeon, a county physician and a matron who managed not only nursing staff, but also most of the support services within the county hospital. This system was disbanded with the formation of the health boards, and health services were subsequently managed by a professional management structure with little or no formal clinical input. Attempting to manage healthcare services without clinicians having direct day-to-day input is something that is not unique to Ireland.

The business of healthcare provision cannot be managed in the same way as most regular businesses are managed. In healthcare, frontline workers, such as nurses, doctors, therapists, social workers and others, are among the most qualified people in the organisation. This is different to what normally pertains in the hierarchical management structure of business, where the workforce at the ground level are often significantly less qualified than those in the management ranks. A further important difference is that, in healthcare, the amount of healthcare provided and the pace of provision of these services is, to a large extent, determined by the frontline professional provider of the service, rather than the customer who is paying for the service. This is the opposite of a normal business model and has to be managed in a very different way.

How is demand for services determined by the professional provider? It is the doctor, therapist or nurse who determines how often the patient needs to be seen and which and how many interventions they have. When I present to my GP with chest pain, he or she determines whether or not the pain is indicative of significant disease, and makes a judgement as to whether or not I need to access other services. If I am referred by my GP to a cardiologist, the cardiologist will determine what investigations I require, which investigations need to be repeated and what interventions, if any, are required. Furthermore, he or she will determine how often I need to attend for ongoing review of symptoms and if any further interventions are required.

In the US, it has been shown that the cost of treating two patients with the same diagnosis and the same complications in a hospital department can vary up to four-fold, depending on which consultant is responsible for providing the patient's care. This relates to the propensity of different consultants to carry out investigations or interventions and also to the length of time patients spend in hospital. Very large studies in the US show a huge variation in the number of X-rays and scans ordered by different consultants for patients with the same condition. The same factors are likely to apply in Ireland. For example, the length of time you stay in hospital in Ireland for various common conditions varies up to two-fold, depending on who your doctor is.

The way professionals practise can, therefore, determine a significant proportion of the costs involved in providing healthcare services. Improving the performance of a healthcare system is dependent on clinicians taking responsibility for the costs they incur. The professional frontline providers also determine the pace at which services are provided. Their practices are central in determining when patients are seen.

In a private business that provides services to the public, the management will focus on improving performance by increasing the speed and quality of service provided by each individual working on the frontline. In a healthcare environment, it is very difficult for a non-clinical manager to seek a better performance from a frontline professional in terms of improving the quality of service or productivity. This is because the frontline healthcare professional can argue that their interaction with each patient is unique and therefore cannot be measured by management as a simple unit of service. Attempts to challenge this argument will generally fail because the professional will insist that a manager cannot interfere with the patient–professional relationship. In addition, they may raise concerns that the safety and quality of the service provided to the patient is being harmed by a manager's attempt to improve performance. Faced with this direct challenge as to patient safety and the professional–patient relationship, it is very difficult for non-clinical managers to improve performance or control expenditure in clinical delivery systems. Only clinicians and other professionals can adequately challenge the performance of their peers, the professional providers of services.

Excluding clinicians from a central role in the management of healthcare services also allows clinicians to abdicate their responsibility for the overall performance of the health services. Clinicians who feel they have been excluded become very comfortable being outside the managerial structure, a position from which they can criticise the performance of management. They see their only responsibility to the healthcare system as being to provide services at an individual level to each patient they treat. They almost always provide such services in a professional manner, which is appreciated by the patient. This appreciation can reinforce the clinician's belief that they have no responsibility for any of the problems that exist in the health service. Any failure in the service can be easily ascribed to others, particularly management.

In essence, clinicians and other professionals live in a world where feedback from their individual patients reassures them that the service they provide as individual professionals is excellent. Although they may have a waiting list that leaves patients waiting several months to access their services, they rarely see themselves as having any responsibility for their waiting list. However, in most cases, waiting lists and other performance issues can only be resolved by clinicians changing the way they work.

Therefore, it was clear from the outset that two of the most important foundation stones for the HSE's transformation programme were the development of clinical leaders to motivate and inspire their colleagues to undertake change, and the development of a performance measurement system that would help clinical leaders to manage their own performance and that of their fellow professionals.

People are often surprised when I link clinical leadership and performance measurement. The reason for this linkage is quite simple. Healthcare professionals (and possibly other professionals) respond first and foremost to peer pressure, especially comparing their own performance to their peers. When the clinical leader has accurate performance information comparing the activity of one professional to another working in the same area, the effect is usually dramatic. Professionals never want to be seen to be underperforming, especially in a situation where they are managed by their peers.

Establishing Clinical Leadership in Ireland

Establishing a clinical leadership model in Ireland was a significant undertaking, as there was no history of structured clinical leadership for the previous three or four decades. This meant that most Irish clinicians did not identify with the need for clinical leadership and greatly valued their independence and the lack of any accountability being applied through a clinical management structure. A medical consultant in Ireland had a very comfortable work environment – you became your own boss at thirty-five to forty years of age, and there was no ongoing evaluation of your performance. It would be a surprise if doctors working under such circumstances rushed to embrace the idea of developing a clinical leadership model. The situation in nursing and in many of the therapies was not as stark in that each had some structure for professional leadership and accountability.

There were a few hospitals in Ireland that had a clinical directorate structure in place, which mainly involved individual specialities. This was based on a UK model of clinical directorates. I had significant concerns about this model becoming our national model for clinical leadership as it did not empower clinicians to manage the healthcare system, but simply had them focus on a specific discipline such as orthopaedics or paediatrics, while the overall system continued to be planned and developed by professional managers. In my view, clinical leadership could only be truly worthwhile and effective if the leaders were, as much as possible, responsible for planning and managing the entire care pathway for patients from when the patient first accessed services.

The negotiation of the new consultant contract (see Chapter 10) provided the opportunity to get agreement from consultants to the introduction of structured clinical leadership in Ireland. At the consultant contract negotiations we were clear that the appointment of clinical directors would be carried out through an independent process, as would be the case with any other appointment, and would not be controlled by consultants themselves. The IHCA were very concerned by this approach. We eventually reached agreement that the first group of clinical directors, who would serve for two years, would be recommended by the clinicians themselves but had to be approved by management. After the first group of clinical directors had served their two-year term all subsequent appointments would be for five years and made through an independent process. This agreement was a significant breakthrough in terms of the potential impact on Irish healthcare.

Following the successful negotiation of the contract, it became a priority for the HSE to plan the appointment of clinical leaders. It was my intention that clinical directors had to be appointed to take responsibility for an entire hospital and play a leading role in planning and developing the interface between the hospital and local community-based services, including primary care. Ultimately, for larger hospitals, one clinical director would not be able to manage all the demands and they would need others reporting to them.

It was essential, even with the appointment of more clinical directors in the larger hospitals, that their posts would be structured based on them having accountability for groups of clinicians likely to be involved in an individual patient's journey. For example, there would be a clinical director responsible for the clinicians who worked in A&E, surgery, anaesthetics and critical care. This would mean that a car accident victim arriving in A&E requiring major surgical and subsequent intensive care support would have their care planned and delivered by a streamlined team-based approach. Another clinical director would be responsible for the medical assessment unit, care of the elderly, medical specialties, coronary care and diagnostics. In this situation, a 75-year-old man with chest pain has his care provided by a team that ensures he is seen by a senior clinician without having to be admitted to hospital, and has all the relevant investigations performed and a treatment plan put in place immediately. This was a very different model to that which operated in the UK at that time, or in the few hospitals in Ireland where clinical directorates existed.

The alternative to establishing the clinical directorate structure in this manner would have been to implement the standard approach by appointing a clinical director for surgery, a clinical director for medicine, a clinical director for obstetrics, etc. The clinical director in a single specialty model can come under pressure from their fellow professionals to maintain loyalty to the discipline, protecting their sectoral interests ahead of any wider institutional or patient care role. This structure could potentially slow down the changes required to improve patient care, rather than drive improvement in the patient journey.

Limiting the number of clinical directors and appointing them to be responsible for hospital catchment areas meant the new directors would be identified as the people who were taking responsibility for improving the quality of care for patients and for enhancing the reputation of their institution. It created a position to which many would aspire, as it would have significant influence on the allocation of resources and the capacity to bring about real change in the experience of patients.

If they were to bring about substantial changes, it was vital that clinical directors had a clinical link all the way up to the HSE's senior management team. We appointed a national leader for clinical directors, who became a member of the senior management team. Dr Barry Whyte, a haematologist at St James's Hospital, was appointed the National Director for Clinical Care and Quality in 2009. Barry had been centrally involved in improving patient care pathways in St James's Hospital, and had led a successful programme of change nationally in the provision of services for patients with haemophilia.

In addition to the hospital-based clinical directors, Barry had to recruit national directors or clinical leads for specific areas. These are responsible for standardising care pathways for various groups of patients, such as patients with a stroke. The most urgent requirement was a general medicine programme, to implement a standardised approach across the country to assessing patients, often elderly, referred by GPs to hospitals each day. These patients were often needlessly admitted to hospital because of the lack of a planned approach to their management.

The consultant representative associations had reservations about this proposed structure. Their understanding of clinical directorates was very different and they expected that a large number of clinical directors would be appointed to provide leadership in individual specialities. There were, however, many senior clinicians who wanted to see changes in the way services were managed and who accepted that measuring and managing the performance of clinicians was necessary if we were to improve services for the public.

We asked fifteen such clinicians who were respected in their own institutions to meet with us to discuss the proposed model of clinical leadership. At the meeting there was significant support for the concept of a small number of clinical leaders focusing on the entire patient journey. The support for this concept by clinicians who were widely respected was a major breakthrough. Without this, it would have been difficult to move clinicians from the concept of clinical directors simply being responsible for an individual specialty or service. The difference between these two approaches was seismic, the latter being focused on trying to maintain the status quo with a little more efficiency, while the former could radically alter the way Irish healthcare services would be planned and developed over the next twenty years.

Engaging with the Postgraduate Colleges

While this group of clinicians were highly respected, they had no formal standing among their peers and could not speak on their behalf. The solution to this problem came from a suggestion by Ms Phil Shovlin, an expert in organisational structure and change management, who also managed my office in the HSE. Her suggestion was to engage with the postgraduate colleges to get their support.

The postgraduate colleges for various medical specialties in Ireland had historically operated as individual organisations. They included the College of Surgeons and the College of Physicians, and, within them, many different faculties such as the Faculty of Paediatrics or the Institute for Obstetricians and Gynaecologists. Many of these groups operated independently of one another. More importantly, they operated with little or no connection to the health services management structure.

The new CEO of the College of Physicians, Leo Kearns, identified that while the College of Physicians had been established in 1654 to improve medical services available to the people of Ireland, its role was now almost solely focused on postgraduate training programmes and examinations. The college had little or no input into planning or improving the quality of the overall health service. In fact, its relationship with the management of the health services in the past had often been somewhat acrimonious.

Leo Kearns was trying to lead the College of Physicians in a new direction, convincing members that they could only have an impact on the quality of the healthcare service if they engaged constructively with the HSE. He and Professor Joseph McKenna, president of the college, saw the need for the different postgraduate colleges to adopt a more unified approach to interacting with the health services. They succeeded in convincing the postgraduate colleges to form the Forum of Irish Postgraduate Training Bodies which would bring together representatives from all training bodies.

This presented an opportunity for us to bring these two processes together, i.e. the postgraduate colleges' focus on having an input into improving the quality of services and the HSE's wish to develop clinical leaders who would spearhead the transformation programme.

Meetings between Leo Kearns, Phil Shovlin and myself took place to discuss how this common agenda might be progressed. The fact that we already had fifteen well-respected clinicians from across the country supporting a proposed model of clinical leadership was a huge benefit. Furthermore, Leo Kearns' experience of management outside healthcare meant that he understood why our approach to clinical leadership had to be different from the old single speciality clinical directorate structure if we were going to bring about worthwhile change from a patient's perspective.

As the secretary of the Postgraduate Forum he discussed our plans with the Forum, and he and the chairman of the Forum, Professor McKenna, engaged very positively with us in developing a process which would allow the Forum to have a central role with the HSE in developing the leadership programme. A joint committee was created between the Postgraduate Forum and the HSE to manage the development of clinical directorates. Monthly meetings of this committee took place, involving representatives of the Postgraduate Forum and senior executives of the HSE. There was great commitment to this process and attendance at the meetings was consistently almost 100 per cent. The fact that this programme was seen as being a priority for both the HSE and the Postgraduate Forum contributed greatly to the speed at which it was advanced.

It was essential that we were able to assure the Forum that this was not an attempt by the HSE to manipulate them in achieving our goals. We had to convince everybody that all of us had the same aim: to improve care for patients in Ireland. We agreed from the beginning that we all had responsibility for the fact that, despite a significant increase in investment over the previous ten years, the services were far from ideal. Once we all accepted this responsibility at an early stage, it was remarkable how quickly people began to focus on building a model of clinical leadership that would improve care for people. The energy created in this group of clinicial leaders and HSE managers was incredible, especially considering the long history of difficult relationships that had existed between the groups.

All involved agreed with the proposal that clinical leadership posts should be small in number and based on the patient care pathway. To ensure compliance with this, a process was established whereby clinical directors could only be appointed with the agreement of a sub-committee of this group. We proceeded to appoint clinical directors. Smaller hospitals were grouped with a larger hospital. Only one clinical director was appointed to each of the large hospitals or groups of hospitals. This sent out a message that clinical directors would have significant power in the management structure.

When these appointments were made, there was no formal management structure into which clinical directors fitted. The HSE was just beginning to develop a new management structure that would manage services in an integrated manner across hospital and community services (see Chapter 14). The Postgraduate Forum and clinical directors subsequently played a central role in designing this structure and determining how clinical directors would fit into the new management structure in terms of delivering integrated care.

It was important to understand everybody's sensitivities during the process of establishing a system of clinical leadership, including those of management. It was my responsibility to convince senior managers that giving clinicians significant executive power in running the health services was essential if we were to succeed in providing the best possible care. Many managers were understandably sceptical at first about the commitment and the capacity of clinicians to undertake such roles. Managers were entering a process where, for example, the CEO of a large hospital was involved in discussions with the Forum on a new approach to healthcare management in which the role of the existing hospital CEOs could be significantly altered and possibly diminished. Regional directors of operations, responsible for managing budgets of €3 billion, were being asked to place huge trust in clinical directors who had not previously been involved in management. It took immense courage on the management side to progress and agree to a clinical leadership structure that greatly empowered clinical directors at executive level in the new integrated management structure (see Chapter 14).

In summary, clinical leaders are essential for a high-performing healthcare service. The introduction of clinical leaders to the Irish healthcare system will be the single most important step in ensuring that Ireland continues to progress with the development of an excellent integrated system for providing healthcare over the next ten to fifteen years because they can:

- Describe and communicate the current and future challenges facing the healthcare system based on the evidence available.
- Make decisions and set the direction that will enable these challenges to be addressed.
- Encourage, motivate, influence, inspire and persuade all relevant stakeholders to embrace new ways of doing things.
- Relentlessly pursue quality improvement with their peers.
- Endorse and celebrate progress with all their clinical and management colleagues.

Chapter 12

Reducing the Cost of Medication in Ireland

The political system and the public regularly complain that public servants are not capable or willing to manage public services in a way that would maximise performance and value for money for taxpayers. From the beginning, the HSE was focused on performance measurement and management and achieving much better value for money for taxpayers. Remarkably, in a healthcare environment, and very much in contrast with the past, the HSE provided above the amount of services contracted for each year in its service plan while remaining within budget up to and including 2010. Outside of staff salaries, the cost of drugs represented the biggest single item of expenditure in the healthcare budget. The account of how the HSE brought about a marked reduction in the cost of medication, outlined in this chapter, illustrates how difficult it is to manage a public service as a business. The political system asks, even demands, that public servants manage more effectively, but the same system can actively undermine the public servants who commit to doing so.

In 2005, at the time of the establishment of the HSE, Ireland was paying more for healthcare than many other European countries, taking into account the young age profile of our population. One reason was that, as in all health services, pay comprises the largest part of healthcare expenditure and salaries were significantly higher in Ireland than in many comparable countries in Europe. National wage agreements between the Government and unions set the pay scales for the public service in general and therefore the HSE was not going to be able to achieve savings in this area. When it was establishing the HSE, the Government reached an agreement with the unions that everyone was not only guaranteed continued employment, but employment in the same location and with the same terms and conditions unless changes were agreed with their union or other representative body (see Chapter 1). This agreement was included in the 2004 Health Act which established the HSE. There was therefore little possibility of reducing expenditure by decreasing the number of people employed in the HSE.

A second area where costs were high in Ireland was pharmaceutical supplies. Medication costs accounted for 11 per cent of public healthcare expenditure in Ireland. Over 30 per cent of the population are covered by the General Medical Scheme (GMS), or medical card scheme, which provides free access to healthcare services and covers the cost of all medications which are supplied to the medical card holder by retail pharmacies. The retail pharmacist reclaims the cost from the HSE. The rest of the population, who are not covered by the medical card scheme, pay for prescribed drugs up to a threshold. This threshold was €85 per month in 2005, and is now €120 per month. Any expenditure by an individual or family above this threshold is paid for by the State through the HSE.

In 2005 the Irish market was one of the most open in the world in terms of allowing access to new drugs. Unlike countries such as the UK, there was at that time no cost–benefit analysis of new drugs prior to their introduction to the Irish market. In an environment that allowed unrestricted access for new, highly expensive, patented medications, and where most of the costs were paid for from the public purse, it was not surprising that the total cost of medication in Ireland had risen dramatically over the previous decade. Between 1995 and 2005, there was an average annual increase of 7.6 per cent in medication costs in Ireland compared to the Organisation for Economic Cooperation and Development (OECD) average of 4.6 per cent. As Ireland has one of the youngest populations in the OECD, you would expect that Ireland would be at the lower end of the spectrum in terms of increasing medication costs. In fact, the opposite was true. Our costs were increasing much quicker than developed countries with much older populations.

In 2007 the HSE paid €1.7 billion for medication. Remarkably, €600 million of this cost was payments to retail pharmacists and wholesalers. The Irish taxpayer was buying a product at a cost of €1.1 billion from the manufacturers and it was costing another €600 million to get the product from the manufacturers to the patient. It was clear that a drugs procurement process that had costs increasing at a rate of almost 8 per cent per year and had distribution costs of about 50 per cent could not be justified. It was only sustainable at the time because significant funds were being diverted from frontline services to support the drugs bill. Money was being consistently moved from supporting the establishment of new services to paying for the increasing cost of medication.

The HSE was determined to get better value for money from the drugs budget. This was essential if we were going to have the resources to maintain existing services and develop new services focused on integrated care. From a governance and probity perspective, it was also the responsibility of the CEO and senior management of the HSE to achieve much better value for taxpayers' money.

Renegotiating the Existing Contracts

The contractual agreements covering the provision of drugs in Ireland had been negotiated between different sectors of the pharmaceutical industry and the Department of Health and Children on a number of occasions over the previous forty years. The cost to the Irish taxpayer associated with the various agreements was enormous when compared to other countries.

The HSE required the expertise of someone who understood the pharmaceutical industry at all levels and who was respected within the industry if it was to successfully negotiate a reduction in the cost of medications. Professor Kamal Sabra was the chief pharmacist at St James's Hospital, Dublin and was internationally recognised for his distinguished academic career. He also had experience of owning and managing retail pharmacies in Ireland and in his home country, Egypt. He had an in-depth understanding of the commercial aspects as well as the clinical aspects of the pharmaceutical industry. He agreed to join the HSE team in 2006. He did this despite the fact that he knew this programme of change was going to make him unpopular with some of his professional colleagues.

The HSE also had within its management ranks a most committed public servant who was an expert on the costs associated with the supply of medication in Ireland. Mr Paddy Burke was and is still responsible for running the primary care reimbursement service, which is responsible for making all payments to pharmacists for drugs dispensed to the public under various schemes. Paddy led an excellent team who had built a comprehensive database with information on payments made for drugs supplied to individual patients by pharmacists. When Paddy Burke's knowledge on payments to different parts of the pharmacy supply chain was combined with Kamal Sabra's professional and business knowledge of the pharmaceutical industry we had a formidable team within the HSE to plan the negotiation of new agreements with various parts of the pharmaceutical supply chain. The team was subsequently joined by Mr Sean Hurley, former CEO of the Southern Health Board, and Mr Ross Hathaway, who was working in the pharmacy contract area of the Department of Health and Children. Ross had a comprehensive understanding of the existing contractual arrangements.

Separate contractual agreements had been agreed in the past by the Department of Health and Children with the different parts of the pharmaceutical industry. The Department had an agreement with the pharmaceutical manufacturers who were largely major multinational companies. Their umbrella group was referred to as the Irish Pharmaceutical Healthcare Association or IPHA.

There were a number of contractual arrangements which had been agreed by the Department with retail pharmacists who were represented by the Irish Pharmaceutical Union (IPU). The most important was for the supply of drugs under the GMS to medical card holders who were entitled to free drugs. Pharmacists were paid a fixed sum per prescribed item. This was portrayed by the IPU as a poor deal from the pharmacists' perspective. However, there were many hidden benefits, outlined below, for pharmacists in having a contract to supply medication to 30 per cent of the population.

The retail pharmacists also received a payment to cover the cost of paying wholesalers to distribute the drugs to them. Pharmacists were paid an additional 17.6 per cent of the manufacturer's list price for medication simply to recompense the wholesalers for distributing drugs from the manufacturers to their pharmacy shops.

It is difficult to understand how an agreement was reached that allowed the charge for a warehousing and distribution service to be calculated as a percentage of the cost of the item. For a distributor the cost of distributing a box of aspirin, costing €1, should be similar to the cost to distribute the same size box containing a new blood cholesterol-lowering agent, costing €100. The agreement resulted in much more being paid for delivering the more expensive box of medication. This resulted in a loss of hundreds of millions of euro over the previous ten years to the Irish taxpayer. However, the wholesale companies were not necessarily the beneficiaries of this largess.

This agreed wholesale distribution payment (17.6 per cent) was paid directly to the retail pharmacist, and they had the responsibility of reimbursing the wholesaler. Everyone was aware that distribution costs were closer to 7 per cent than the 17.6 per cent negotiated with the Government. Retail pharmacists, therefore, negotiated much lower payments with the wholesalers for the distribution of drugs. As a result, a significant proportion of the fee paid by the taxpayer for the distribution of drugs was not paid to wholesalers but was retained by the retail pharmacist. The wholesaler presumably agreed to this arrangement in order to maintain the business of supplying the pharmacy. Larger pharmacies were able to retain a bigger proportion of the 17.6 per cent, between 7 and 10 per cent, because of the competitive nature of the wholesale business. In addition, pharmacists negotiated reductions with the manufacturers based on the volume of drugs sold, but charged the manufacturer's list price when claiming reimbursement from the HSE for supplying medical card holders.

Retail pharmacies also provided medication to the public who were not covered by the GMS. The patient or customer paid the pharmacy directly for the medication until they reached a threshold (€85 a month in 2007). Beyond this threshold, the pharmacy was reimbursed by the HSE for any further drugs dispensed to the family or individual. Payments for these services were based on a flat fee for each item prescribed, plus a 50 per cent mark-up on the cost of the medications. Again, this 50 per cent mark-up applied to the manufacturer's list price for the medication, regardless of the actual cost charged by the manufacturer to the pharmacist. The arrival of an expensive new patented drug on the Irish market resulted in windfall profits for retail pharmacies because of this 50 per cent mark-up. This resulted in new patented drugs on the Irish market being much more expensive than was necessary.

Therefore, when supplying medications to a customer who had exceeded the drug payment scheme threshold, the pharmacist benefited from (i) a prescription fee for each item, (ii) a 50 per cent mark-up on the cost of the medication, (iii) a rebate of approximately 8 per cent from the payment to wholesalers who supplied the medication, and (iv) a negotiated reduction in the cost of the drugs from the manufacturers based on the volumes they purchased. All of these were paid for by the HSE.

There was a lot of evidence to suggest that the retail pharmacy business model was benefiting enormously from the taxpayer-funded contracts. Pharmacies in the Republic of Ireland were being sold at four times the price paid for a similar-sized business in Northern Ireland. In the Republic of Ireland pharmacy shops were sold for three times their turnover, whereas comparable pharmacies in Northern Ireland were being sold for 0.7 times their turnover.

When the HSE began to highlight the high costs associated with the supply of medications in Ireland there was a willingness by the pharmaceutical manufacturers to accept that a fairer arrangement was required. However, the IPU, representing the retail pharmacists, portrayed our actions as being unfair and accused the HSE of undermining their businesses.

Our negotiations to obtain a reduction in payments for the supply of medications involved the different parts of the supply chain.

(i) The Manufacturers

Negotiations with the IPHA took place in 2006 and were constructive overall. There was an acceptance by the IPHA that the health services needed to reduce the cost of medications, but obviously they were determined to minimise this reduction. Nevertheless, agreement was reached in a relatively short space of time, and covered two specific areas: older drugs that were coming off patent and newly developed drugs. In the case of older drugs an agreement was reached that the cost of these medications would be reduced by 35 per cent overall: 20 per cent six months after the agreement was signed and a further 15 per cent twenty-two months later. It was estimated that this would lead to a reduction of approximately €80 million annually in the cost of medicines.

When a new drug was patented and launched on the market, Irish prices had traditionally been set based on the average price across five other developed countries. The countries used to set the price for Ireland did not include Spain, which had much lower medication costs. Agreement was reached that the number of countries used to set the price for Ireland would be expanded to include nine, one of which would be Spain. Therefore, the cost of new medications in Ireland will in future be based on a much broader and fairer international comparison. The effect of this change will not be obvious for a number of years, as new drugs are developed and brought to market, but it will lead to significant reductions in the cost of very expensive new drugs.

(ii) Wholesale Distribution of Medication

When it came to the distribution and retailing of drugs in Ireland, the HSE, as a large purchaser, is considered to be in a monopoly position. Therefore, the HSE had to conform with European regulations for a monopoly purchaser. These European regulations require that, under such circumstances, the purchaser must go through a formal process to ensure a fair and reasonable price is set for the service that is being provided. This required the HSE to engage an independent company to undertake an assessment of the pharmaceutical supply chain and to determine what would be a reasonable charge for the distribution of drugs from the manufacturer to the retailer. The recommendation was that, while the cost associated with distribution was likely to amount to less than 8 per cent, the HSE should agree to pay 8 per cent in view of the very significant reduction that this represented from the existing 17.6 per cent, which would require a major readjustment for the businesses involved. This reduction in the distribution costs was estimated to generate €100 million per annum in savings.

This change should not have affected the wholesalers, who, in any event, were receiving a lot less from the retail pharmacists than the 17.6 per cent allowed for in the agreements. However, one of the three major wholesalers was owned by a group of retail pharmacists and a different wholesaler owned several retail outlets. Therefore, there was, in fact, no real distinction between wholesalers and many retailers in the case of a large number of pharmacy outlets.

We proceeded with plans to implement the new wholesale distribution payment of 8 per cent with effect from 1 March 2008. It was a significant step forward for the HSE, pending the development of a whole new contractual relationship.

(iii) Retail Pharmacy Services

In early 2008, the HSE commenced a comprehensive review of the services required from retail pharmacy contractors as part of the planning process for the development and implementation of new contractual arrangements with them. We proposed that a flat fee should be applied to each item dispensed by pharmacists and that this fee should take into account all of the pharmacists' professional services, including advice provided to clients. This would remove the link between the cost of medication and the payment for services to pharmacists. It would discontinue the situation whereby higher payments had to be made to the pharmacists for dispensing more expensive drugs. The introduction of a flat fee for every item prescribed would ensure pharmacists were remunerated equally well, irrespective of whether they dispensed an expensive or a low cost medication.

Compliance with EU legislation again meant the HSE would have to carry out a public consultation process to determine what prescription fee per item should be paid. A firm of economic consultants had to be commissioned to provide an independent economic analysis of what would be a fair dispensing fee.

While this process was underway, the IPU continued a public relations and political lobbying campaign. This campaign was incredibly successful with political parties, the media and the public. Each pharmacist in their local area lobbied their customers, who, as in any health professional–client interaction, are very thankful for the services they receive. Public anxiety was also raised by the suggestion from the IPU that pharmacy shops in smaller communities would close. This frightened elderly people especially and also raised concerns in political circles that they would face a backlash in future elections if pharmacies in small towns closed. While we at the HSE tried to make the counterargument, including the fact that pharmacies in the Republic of Ireland were being sold for four times the amount paid for equivalent pharmacies in Northern Ireland, we failed to convince the public that we were acting in their interest.

At a number of meetings of the Oireachtas Joint Committee on Health and Children, the HSE was criticised by politicians from all parties about the unfairness of our approach to reducing the cost of drugs. On 14 November 2007, the committee met with representatives of the IPU, who made an extensive presentation on their objection to the HSE's action. By the end of the meeting, most of the politicians had expressed their dissatisfaction with the HSE. Surprisingly, the committee meeting took place with no counter view being presented by the HSE or any other expert input to challenge the claims made by the IPU. Subsequently, the HSE was represented at a special meeting on this issue on 12 February 2008 by Kamal Sabra, Sean Hurley and Paddy Burke. They were subjected to a robust challenge by politicians from all political parties. The HSE and its negotiators were portrayed by many as an apparatus of State undermining local pharmacies. The State's political system appeared to accept that the provision of a reasonable service justified the taxpayer paying extremely high rates for it. It seemed to go unnoticed that the HSE team was representing the interest of the taxpayers in trying to reduce expenditure on drugs, which was out of line with most comparable countries and which was resulting in a reduction in other frontline services. In retrospect, much of this presumably reflected the economic buoyancy of the country at that time and a lack of a sense of responsibility for managing taxpayers' money in a prudent fashion.

The determination of the HSE team to pursue value for money in relation to the contracts that existed with the pharmaceutical industry was commendable. The personal toll that this took on them was considerable. They found it difficult to understand why they should be the subject of criticism by politicians when they were in fact defending the public interest. It is difficult to see what incentive there is for public servants to protect the taxpayers' interest by challenging excessive levels of expenditure when the outcome is that such public servants are portrayed as unreasonable and incompetent. The transcripts from this meetings would be of significant interest to those who study performance in the public service. These are available at www.oireachtas.ie.

The reduction in the cost of drugs agreed with the manufacturers was introduced in 2007. The reduction from 17.6 per cent to 8 per cent in the payment to cover wholesale distribution costs was implemented in early

2008. However, before we could introduce the third and final change, the proposed flat fee to be paid per item dispensed by retail pharmacists, court actions by various pharmacists stalled the process.

The Hickey case was the first to be heard. To the HSE's surprise, the action was initiated because of the HSE's decision to reduce the amount paid to cover the cost of wholesale distribution from 17.6 per cent to 8 per cent. This was a payment for wholesalers and not retailers and yet the retailers were initiating the action to stop this change. This confirmed as outlined earlier that retailers, rather than wholesalers, retained much of this payment from the State.

The Hickey group, as plaintiffs, put forward the case that the payment of the wholesale reimbursement rate was an 'implied term' in their contract, which had been established among other things by custom and practice and that, although it related to payment to another group, the wholesalers, it could not, they insisted, be changed without the agreement of the retail pharmacists. They claimed that, by unilaterally reducing the wholesale mark-up, the HSE was in breach of what they referred to as the implied terms of their contract. This case put forward by the pharmacists essentially accepted that a significant amount of taxpayers' money expended over many years, specifically to cover the costs of wholesale distribution, was in fact being retained by retail pharmacists in return for no service provision.

The judgment that was delivered in the Hickey case found that the HSE did not have the power to make any alteration in payments to pharmacists because this power was not transferred to the HSE at the time of its establishment by the Government. It found that the Minister alone had the power to change payments to pharmacies. From the perspective of the HSE, this meant that the savings could not be achieved immediately and this was a setback. However, the rest of the judgment was extremely positive from the HSE's perspective. The judge found the Minister for Health, as the individual still responsible for the contract, which was negotiated by the Department of Health and Children prior to the establishment of the HSE, had unilateral power within the terms of the existing contract to change payments, and that all that was required was for the Minister to consult with the pharmacists before making such changes. This was a fundamental finding as it meant that the State in the future could alter such contracts following consultation rather than negotiation.

The judge also specifically stated that contractors should not accept any payment or consideration other than those received from the HSE under the standard contract. This suggested that the receipt of rebates from manufacturers, while billing the HSE for the full cost of drugs or retaining part of the cost allowed to cover the wholesale distribution of medicines, was in breach of the pharmacy contract.

As a result of this judgement, the HSE had to reinstate the 17.6 per cent payment for wholesale distribution costs and to repay arrears for the period of time that the 8 per cent rate was in place. However, the judgment also made it clear that, by operating through the Minister, the HSE could bring about the changes that it wanted to implement.

The Minister then established an independent process under Mr Seán Dorgan to look at pricing. The outcome of this process yielded essentially the same savings as the HSE proposals but through a somewhat different mechanism. Instead of reducing the wholesale rate from 17.6 per cent to 8 per cent, it was proposed to reduce it to 10 per cent (it has subsequently been reduced to 8 per cent). In order to bring about savings equivalent to our proposal, the mark-up applied on non-GMS prescriptions by pharmacists was reduced from 50 per cent to 20 per cent. At the same time, an enhanced fee for dispensing items prescribed for all patients was introduced. These changes would yield savings of over €100 million per annum.

The Minister signed off on the new proposals put forward by the independent body. However the IPU chose not to accept the proposals and instead some members proceeded to give notice of resignation from their contracts with the HSE. This was designed to increase public pressure on the HSE by suggesting to the public that they would no longer be able to avail of pharmacy services through State schemes such as the medial card scheme.

The HSE believed that many pharmacies would not withdraw these services from the public. We were confident that there were many pharmacists across the country who would not take action that would inconvenience their customers. Furthermore, some large multinational pharmacy chains had opened in Ireland, and they were unlikely to engage in this dispute with the HSE.

Following the announcement of the change in payments, 813 of the approximately 1,600 pharmacists who had State contracts wrote to the HSE giving notice of termination of their contracts as of August 2009. The pharmacists were immediately asked by the HSE to confirm in writing that they were definitely withdrawing from their contractual arrangement. As a result of this request, a significant degree of concern seemed to arise among pharmacists that if they withdrew from the contract with the HSE they might not be given new contracts subsequent to any future settlement. Remarkably, 343 of the terminations were immediately withdrawn.

The Government were, however, very concerned that withdrawal of a large number of pharmacists from State-sponsored schemes would result in a significant backlash from the public. We in the HSE took the view that we could not back down from implementing these very significant reductions in expenditure simply because of the pharmacists' threat to withdraw from the schemes. We were under significant pressure from all across the political spectrum to reach a compromise, except from the Minister for Health who continued to support our stance.

The Government asked the HSE for reassurance that it had contingency plans in place for August 2009 so that would be able to deal with the withdrawal of services by pharmacists. It would have been impossible for the HSE to provide an adequate contingency plan if retail pharmacy services were withdrawn all across the country. However, we knew that pharmacists also operated in a competitive environment within towns and cities across Ireland, especially where international chains had entered the market. If even one pharmacist remained open among several in one town the dispute would, we believed, be undermined. We therefore tried to reassure the Government that we believed the IPU would focus on withdrawing services in very isolated areas where little competition existed and where it would therefore be possible for them to ensure that all services were withdrawn in that area.

This assessment of the situation was correct. In July 2009, the IPU succeeded in withdrawing all services in some rural parts of Ireland, especially in large areas of Donegal, Mayo and Kerry. Elsewhere, across the country, many pharmacies did not open in the early stages of the dispute, but enough remained open to ensure continuity of service for the public. Under the leadership of Paddy Burke and Laverne McGuinness, the national director for integrated services, the HSE had, from July 2009, a comprehensive contingency plan in place for covering the regions where services were totally withdrawn. Pharmacists were recruited nationally and internationally. Pharmacies were established in buildings on HSE sites in the affected regions. HSE management and staff from across several different areas in the organisation supported the new pharmacy units. They worked extra long days and over weekends for no extra pay in order to ensure the public continued to get their medication.

The contingency plan was challenged. Some of the wholesalers made it difficult for the HSE to get supplies of drugs, while, at the same time, IPU members appeared on several media programmes declaring that the outlets opened by the HSE did not have all the stock required and therefore were putting patients at risk. There was also an orchestrated campaign to overrun the new centres with an artificially created demand for medication. However, operating under these somewhat siege-like conditions, the contingency pharmacy units and the logistical centres set up to supply them performed heroically. The workforce developed a common purpose in their determination to deliver the required services to people in small rural communities. This extended to individual pharmacists and others from these contingency centres travelling out at night to people in their homes in isolated areas to ensure they got the correct medication. Transport was also arranged by the HSE to bring people to the nearest pharmacy in isolated areas.

It would be difficult for the public to understand how well served they were by HSE public servants who remained determined in the face of enormous pressure to maintain pharmacy services for the public. Over a period of a few weeks, it became clear that the HSE contingency service was working well and that the dispute was not achieving its goals. With each passing day, more and more pharmacists reopened their shops.

We were now finally in a position to implement the contract changes that would yield very significant savings in the drugs budget. The total saving at that time amounted to €200 million per year, and is now significantly greater.

Generic Prescribing

Many commentators over the years called on the HSE to deal with the high drugs bill by making the prescribing of generic medications compulsory. Generic medications are those that are manufactured, following the expiry of a drugs patent protection, by companies that did not own the original patent on the drug. They are copies which, post-patent, can be legally made to the exact standard of the original, and are generally sold internationally at a fraction of the cost of the original patented medication.

At first glance, compulsory prescribing of generic medication seems like an easy way to markedly reduce the bill for medicines. Unfortunately, this is not the case. Drugs available in generic form in Ireland account for only 15 per cent of the overall cost of medicines. In 2008, reducing the payment for all such medicines in Ireland to the cost of the cheapest equivalent generic drug available in Ireland would have saved €23 million from a budget of almost €2 billion.

While even this saving would have been welcome, potential reductions associated with enforcing compulsory prescribing of generic medications are undermined by the fact that, in Ireland, the cost of generic medication is extremely high. As part of the INFO price project, all EU member states submit price information every six months for fifteen products and their cheapest generic equivalent. In December 2008, Ireland was one of the countries that submitted ex-factory prices for such drugs. In 80 per cent of cases, Ireland was either the most expensive or the second most expensive country.

The price differences were dramatic. In 2008, the retail cost of Simvastatin, a widely prescribed cholesterol-lowering agent, in generic form was fifty times higher in Ireland than in the Netherlands, thirty times higher here than in Denmark, and twenty-five times higher here than in the UK. Omeprazole, an agent that reduces acid secretion in the stomach, had a similar price differential: it was forty times more expensive to purchase in Ireland than in Holland, seventeen times more expensive than in the UK, and thirteen times more expensive than in Denmark. All of this might suggest that the manufacturers and distributors of generic drugs in Ireland are highly inefficient. This is not the case. Generic medications are invoiced to Irish retail pharmacists at this high cost, and most of this cost is paid through the HSE schemes by the taxpayer. Subsequently, despite the fact that the HSE or taxpayer has reimbursed the full cost of the drugs to the retail pharmacist, very significant rebates are given to retail pharmacists by the generic manufacturer. As a result, the Irish taxpayer is paying large sums of money for medication that the manufacturer is in reality supplying at a cost markedly below the invoiced cost.

It is, therefore, not a surprise that the IPU were always to the forefront in claiming that the HSE should focus on making prescribing of generic medications mandatory. This campaign had a number of benefits from their perspective. First, it brought focus on to the 15 per cent of the drug bill, diverting attention from the 85 per cent that the HSE was focusing on. Second, it would yield at maximum €23 million in savings compared to the overall savings of €200 million that were achieved. Finally, of course, the profit margin for pharmacists on generics was, for the reasons outlined above, often in excess of the equivalent drugs supplied by the original manufacturers.

The next phase in the drug pricing strategy was, therefore, to focus on setting what is referred to as a reference price for drugs when the patent has expired. This is a maximum price that the State would pay through any of its schemes for a particular medication, whether generic or not. This still needs to be introduced. Once the reference price is set, there will be transparency across the supply chain and the taxpayer will be protected from exploitation.

There is no denying that some pharmacists face significant financial challenges as a result of these changes. Anyone who purchased a pharmacy business for three times its turnover clearly did so based on a proposed business model that saw the HSE continuing to pay the very high reimbursement fees that had existed for years under the old healthcare management system.

There are, however, great opportunities for pharmacists to play a much greater role in the provision of health services in Ireland. Pharmacists are highly qualified and skilled healthcare professionals who can provide many more services in an integrated community-focused healthcare system. They can play major roles in areas varying from screening and treatment programmes for chronic diseases like hypertension and diabetes to the administration of vaccines. They could become central figures in multidisciplinary primary care teams.

Change, once again, was unpopular. As with most other elements of the transformation programme, our actions in reducing the cost to the Exchequer of drugs generated opposition, especially from members of the Dáil, rather than support for the HSE. It was also difficult to convince the public that we were acting in their interest, due to the very successful public relations campaign, organised over a prolonged period, by the IPU, who portrayed the HSE management as unfairly driving the pharmacy shops across the country out of business. We should perhaps not be surprised that public representatives showed little support for an organisation that was trying to save public money in the boom years of 2006 and 2007. While the public and politicians were frightened by the spectre of local pharmacies closing because of the HSE's focus on reducing prices, the number of pharmacy businesses registered in Ireland had increased to 1,728 in 2010, compared with 1,628 in 2007.

Chapter 13

Introducing Performance Management – The Design of HealthStat

The whole idea of performance management sounds very commercial and uncaring. So why is performance measurement and management important in healthcare?

Consider the following scenario. Daniel is an eight-year-old boy who has difficulty pronouncing some words, and recently this difficulty has made him feel embarrassed at school. His GP refers him to the local speech and language therapy service. His parents are informed that it will be ten months before he sees a speech and language therapist. His cousin Rachel lives in another part of Ireland and had a similar problem two years earlier. At that time, she received an appointment to start therapy with the local speech and language unit two weeks after referral by her GP. After an initial assessment, she and her parents were invited to a group session with other families, where the therapist could help six to eight families at any one time.

Daniel's parents contact their local health centre again and ask if they can join group therapy sessions. They are told that group treatment is not provided by the speech and language services in their area, and no consideration has been given to providing such services. The health service management in the area Daniel lives in are unaware that in other areas, such as where Rachel lives, each speech and language therapist treats more children than in their area. They are also unaware that there is evidence to show that group sessions are very effective in treating many children referred for speech and language therapy.

This type of scenario is not unique to speech and language therapy, but applies right across the services. An elderly person requiring eye surgery because of a cataract has to undergo the often frightening experience of being admitted to hospital for a few days in one area of Ireland, whereas he or she could have the surgery performed as a day patient in another area.

A national performance measurement system is essential if we are to ensure that high quality and efficient professional practices are in place throughout the health service, rather than being available in sporadic locations, depending on the initiative and leadership of a local healthcare professional or therapist. The introduction of a comprehensive performance measurement and management system – HealthStat – by the HSE in 2008 has resulted in many innovative and effective clinical practices being implemented consistently across the country for the benefit of patients. Performance management may sound cold and dispassionate, but it is in fact central to care and compassion for patients.

As noted earlier, when I was first asked to consider the post of CEO of the HSE I identified two issues as major priorities if we were to make progress in transforming the service. The first priority was to develop clinical leadership, whereby the performance of our services would be managed and driven to a large extent at the frontline by professionals themselves. The second requirement was to introduce a performance measurement system that would allow us to bring about robust performance management in a health and social care environment. These priorities were interdependent. It is impossible for clinicians to manage their peers in the absence of performance measurements. When, however, good performance measures are available at an individual professional level, managing clinical performance becomes relatively straightforward as professionals respond very quickly to having any underperformance highlighted. Furthermore, professionals who are performing at a very high level are happier working within the health and social care system when they can see that their efforts to improve services are being acknowledged.

Performance management is critical in driving the effective operation of any business. Across the world many healthcare systems struggle to create a culture of performance management. One of the reasons for this may be that performance management systems used in healthcare are modelled on performance management strategies used in regular business enterprises. This ignores the fact mentioned so often in this book that the business of healthcare is very different to practically any other business in that demand for services and the pace of service delivery is often not driven by the customer but rather by the provider. So the performance management system that is applied has to be different.

Traditional Performance Measures

Traditionally in Ireland, we collected large amounts of healthcare activity data, but it would be difficult to refer to most of these measures as indicators of effective performance. Most of the data was collected for monthly monitoring reports required by the Department of Health and Children in areas like the number of attendances at A&E and outpatient departments, and the number of patients admitted to hospital.

The system was based on the assumption that increased activity was an indicator of better performance. This is a fundamental misconception when one is measuring performance in a healthcare environment. Healthcare professionals, as providers in the healthcare system, can increase or decrease the amount of output at any given time. Measuring performance in this manner can incentivise healthcare systems and healthcare professionals to increase activities which are not necessarily effective from a patient's perspective and drive up costs.

Using increased activity as an indicator of improved performance may encourage services to become efficient at doing the wrong thing. Rewarding hospitals for increasing the number of overnight patients admitted, or for an increase in the number of patients who attend the hospital's emergency department, or the outpatient department, are all examples of this. Effective hospitals providing high quality care would establish an integrated approach with community services to reduce A&E and outpatient attendances, and would focus on increasing day case work and improving access to diagnostics in a manner that would reduce overnight admissions. Performance systems that are totally based on increased activity levels penalise providers who improve their effectiveness by introducing a more integrated approach, rewarding instead those who adhere to old models of care.

Performance measurement in healthcare should be focused on ensuring that patients get high quality treatment in the right place and at the right time. Often the right treatment may be for no intervention to occur. Assessing an individual professional's performance as having improved on the basis of them increasing the number of interventions performed on patients can, in fact, undermine the quality of care and harm some patients. For example, interventions such as coronary artery stents, colonoscopies and MRI scans are not necessarily always good for patients. However, these interventions are more likely to be provided in a system which rewards such activity, particularly with monetary compensation, while providing little recognition for the medical professional who practices in a holistic way and takes the time to determine if such interventions are necessary or in the best interests of the patient.

Another interesting practice in the old system was the use of measures that, while rewarding increased throughput of patients, did not consider the length of time it took patients to access these services. For example, prior to the HSE, no record was kept of the waiting times for patients referred to hospital outpatient departments by GPs. It could be argued that all performance measures relating to access should be based on how quickly the patient is seen and have little or nothing to do with how many patients are seen. The number of patients who need to attend as outpatients can be significantly reduced if an integrated approach to care is adopted, including the introduction of standardised care pathways for use by hospital-based and community-based professionals managing common chronic diseases. These are the types of activities that our performance measures should reward.

Measuring Individual and Team Performance

Performance measurements in the Irish healthcare service, prior to the establishment of the HSE, were focused on the output of large units such as hospitals. Measuring performance at this high level is of some interest but, ultimately, in a system based on the delivery of services by frontline professionals, such measures are of limited use in performance management. Clinicians may be aware of the underperformance of the unit that they work in, but may have little insight into any responsibility they have for the poor performance. This is all the more so because they are meeting patients on a day-to-day basis who reassure them as to the excellent service they provide for them as individuals. In such an environment, it is only possible to bring about change by having measures reflect performance at an individual professional level.

The majority of professionals like to get feedback on their individual performance. Measurement at this level allows the professional to identify problems with their performance, or, as mentioned, to be recognised by their peers when their performance is exceptional. The latter is extremely important as high-performing clinicians in a system which, overall, has a poor level of performance will ultimately become demoralised. I always believed that if we could provide professionals with individual performance measures they themselves would alter their care pathways to improve performance, for instance by reducing the number of review patients coming to their clinics or increasing the amount of day surgery they performed. It is almost impossible to bring about these changes, or at least exceptionally slow, when you use normal management systems with frontline professionals.

Establishing Performance Measurement and Management

The challenge for healthcare and social care systems is to develop performance measures that are relevant to professionals both individually and as members of teams within hospitals and community services. Good performance management is dependent on the accuracy and reproducibility of the measures that are used to determine the effectiveness of service provision. The measures must be unambiguous and fair, with national or international benchmarks as targets. Measures must have credibility with those who work in the service and be acceptable to them. They must be easy to audit to ensure that data is comparable across different centres. Everybody must be able to see that there is equity in the application of the measures. If the measures lack credibility with frontline care providers, either in terms of how reliable they are or how consistently they are measured across different parts of the service, then it will be very difficult to get buy-in to using these measures as part of a performance management system. Input by frontline professionals into establishing the measures and determining how returns are audited is essential if such credibility is to be established. The system, therefore, has to be a dynamic process where clinicians and managers have an opportunity to put forward their views as to why their performance is as it is and can challenge and, if justified, change the performance measures that are applied to them.

Equally, the system can only function well if there is professional peer review of performance. This is particularly important as healthcare professionals will often be able to suggest that their practice is different in terms of the type or complexity of patients they see, thereby justifying a variance in performance, if the system is evaluated by managers without input from their peers. The system has to make frontline professionals accountable in front of their peers so that explanations for underperformance can be honestly evaluated.

The ambition for the HSE was to move from a system that had little experience of relevant performance measurement and, therefore, performance management to developing what would evolve into a state-of-the-art approach to performance management in health and social care.

Having been offered the post of CEO, I met Maureen Lynott, who was the first CEO of the National Treatment Purchase Fund (NTPF) in Ireland, a government agency established to deal with waiting lists for elective procedures in hospitals. The NTPF organised for patients on hospital waiting lists to have their procedures carried out, usually in another institution. This was initially seen as a significant interference with the doctor–patient relationship, and some of the representative bodies for doctors were opposed to the NTPF. Furthermore, hospitals were not all happy with the idea that their patients were to have their procedures carried out at other institutions. Initially, a large amount of resistance built up through this alliance of clinicians and hospitals to the work that Maureen was doing through the NTPF. However, over a period of two years she established a successful waiting list initiative. She implemented a rigorous approach to measuring waiting lists and insisting that patients waiting over a certain period of time had their records transferred to the NTPF.

I was concerned that establishing a performance management system was also going to meet some resistance because of the understandable fear of performance improvement systems. We could not afford to take several years negotiating the introduction of such a system. The professional bodies and hospitals across the country had developed respect for

Maureen, based on her work as CEO of the NTPF, and so I believed she would be the ideal person to develop and help implement a performance measurement and management approach for our healthcare service.

Building the HealthStat System

In 2005, we quickly realised that, although a huge amount of data was being collected by the various parts of the health service each month for the Department, there were no audit systems in place to provide any reassurance as to the accuracy of the measurements. Everybody seemed to be happy enough if a performance monitoring report could be provided each month to the Department, and the Department seemed to be quite happy as long as they received a set of figures.

The HSE had to develop a performance measurement system that would be relevant to both healthcare professionals and management, and which would allow performance to be managed in a dynamic way, with both clinicians and managers involved. Most importantly, the measures chosen would incentivise the changes that were required to develop an integrated healthcare service. We looked at systems in other countries such as the UK and found there was a lot to be learned from parts of individual systems already in place in different countries. However, it was when looking at performance measurement outside of the healthcare system that Maureen Lynott discovered CitiStat, a performance measurement and management system in operation in the city of Baltimore in the US. CitiStat evolved from an earlier system put in place by the New York City Police Department, which was adopted for use by the Mayor and his executive in Baltimore.

Maureen and a small group of people visited the CitiStat unit in Baltimore and attended some of their meetings. CitiStat was based on documenting performance measures across areas such as refuse collection, policing, parks and estate maintenance. However, the unique part of CitiStat was that the senior managers responsible for each of these areas met on a monthly basis in a forum chaired by the Mayor. He would discuss and praise or challenge them on the performance of their individual services and a log of follow-up actions was maintained to ensure that any necessary actions occurred. This interactive process could address our requirement to have a system that would not only measure and help manage performance, but would do so with the active involvement of the managers and clinicians themselves. Such a system would allow us to leverage one of the most important determinants of change: peer comparison in a professional environment.

We were under pressure to advance this project quickly as in the absence of a successful performance measurement and management system it was extremely difficult to get transformation started, such as reconfiguring hospitals and improving the effectiveness of our services in hospitals and the community.

The first requirement was to set up a HealthStat unit in the HSE. Mr Mark Turner was recruited from industry because of his experience in working in a performance improvement environment. Mark played a critical role initially in working with our staff up and down the country in individual professional groups and units to obtain their buy-in to the overall process. We had to reassure them that this was an inclusive process, that we would listen to their input and also that this process could significantly enhance our services to the public.

The HealthStat Forum was established in an almost identical manner to the CitiStat Forum in Baltimore, ensuring that all of the relevant stakeholders are present or represented at each meeting. Each hospital had three representatives, the CEO/manager, clinical director and nursing director. Also present were the representatives from the community services for the area. The development of integrated services areas, as described in Chapter 14, significantly enhances the capacity of HealthStat to drive change, as the professionals and managers are then responsible for the performance of the entire service.

The HealthStat Forum was chaired by me, as CEO of the HSE. While the commitment of the CEO to the process is important in getting buy-in from others, it is even more important that there are clinicians on the corporate management team to lead the discussions at the Forum. Clinicians are required to interrogate specific performance figures and to ensure that there is an honest debate in terms of any explanation put forward by individual parts of the service as to why their performance is not reaching an adequate level. Equally, when valid reasons are put forward to explain variations in performance, it is important that the HealthStat Forum has the capacity to accept that these are valid concerns and respond to them.

The challenge in developing performance measures for use in an interactive system like this was to identify a small number of relevant measures in each of the three priority areas: (i) access to services, (ii) integration of services within the community and between community-based services and hospitals, and (iii) optimal use of resources. This is challenging because professionals often insist that a very wide array of measures are taken into account in the belief that these are required to give an accurate reflection of the breadth and depth of their work. This is an understandable concern, but it is also known that systems using large numbers of measures in performance management can be counterproductive, because of the wide array of measures that have to be collected and, more importantly, interpreted. We had to convince professionals that there was good evidence internationally that a relatively small number of performance measures could be accurate in indicating overall performance.

Initially, we identified measures that had already been validated internationally and provided the justification from the literature for the use of these measures. There was also a need to develop measures that were specific to the Irish healthcare service, particularly where significant problems existed in the effectiveness of the services. We developed these measures ourselves and then used the HealthStat process to discuss and, if any inconsistencies in the measures were identified, refine them. These included fairly straightforward measures, such as the length of time a patient referred from their GP had to wait to have an ultrasound, or the length of time people waited for access to physiotherapy or child and adolescent mental health services. More controversially, we measured the number of children seen by teams, such as child and adolescent mental health teams, or the number of hospital outpatients seen per consultant. These are more controversial measures because the experience and skill-mix of the team can have an impact on them.

We had to accept that some of these measures were crude initially, but we were able to earn buy-in to their use by reassuring the individual services and professionals that we would work continuously with them through the HealthStat process to refine and improve the measures. This engagement was critical in building confidence in HealthStat.

Our initial focus was on hospital measurement systems because that was where staff were already collecting activity data and also where internationally standardised measures were available to us. Measures of performance at a community level in areas such as mental health services, public health nursing, social work and child protection were, to a large extent, not available.

As we established systems to measure performance in community-based services we learned that there were very significant variations in performance due to individual professional practices. This included the example outlined earlier of speech and language therapy, where waiting lists could be long in some areas compared to others with the same population, despite there being an equal number of speech and language therapists. On investigating this in the HealthStat Forum, it became clear that the differences were due to differences in professional practice, where in some areas therapists operated group therapy sessions for appropriate children where several children and their families attended at a single session, whereas in other areas all children were dealt with as individuals. The Forum was then able to ask for a review of the evidence for each system. There was evidence to show that group therapy was effective for certain children and also that the children and their families were positive about the group approach. This is an excellent example of how a dynamic process allows for individual measures of performance to be discussed by professional peer groups and the evidence and outcome for different practices assessed by them with changes in practice being subsequently implemented across the country.

At the Forum, similar experiences began to arise in many other areas, such as variations in outpatient waiting lists for orthopaedic surgeons. At the Forum meeting, some hospitals showed how they dramatically reduced waiting lists for orthopaedic surgery clinics when it was agreed that selected referrals were first evaluated by physiotherapists, who could reassure or treat and discharge the vast majority of patients referred to them without these patients needing to see the orthopaedic surgeon. While this was happening in some areas, in others all referrals were first seen by the orthopaedic surgeon, and therefore many patients remained on a waiting list for a consultation they did not need. These are just a couple of examples of how effective a process like this can be, and how constructive it can be in bringing about changes in professional practices.

The response from clinicians and managers who were involved with the HealthStat process was surprising in terms of how widely welcomed the approach was. Initially, we were concerned that presenting performance data and evaluating performance might result in a defensive response from professionals. The opposite was true. Rapidly managers and clinical leaders began to see this as a very positive experience and that the process could support them in performance managing their services much more successfully. It provided them with information about the performance of services which had not been available before, including peer comparison figures that they could take back to their units and use with their individual practitioners to improve performance. Equally, it often gave them positive feedback for good performance. It allowed them to benchmark themselves nationally, and some were identified as leaders nationally in specific areas of service provision.

It was decided at an early stage that the HeathStat measures would be made available to the public and be placed on the internet. However, a decision was made that the figures would not be put up until one year after the initiation of the process. This was to allow time to ensure, based on feedback from individual units, that the measures were fair and that the information being collected was accurate. Again, this approach built confidence that the process was not about criticising individuals but rather about trying to constructively improve performance. It was about spreading good practice across the system, and establishing more effective and standardised approaches to the way in which we provided services in Ireland.

HealthStat is still very much a developing system, which is of significant interest to other healthcare services internationally. It must now focus more on developing patient outcome measures which include not only what was done to a patient, but how effective the intervention was. The public should be insisting that such measures are easily available to them. This type of transparency is essential if we are to achieve the best quality of care.

So did HealthStat make any difference to the performance of the healthcare service? The evidence confirms that it had a significant effect. Each month, a traffic light indicator – green, orange or red – is given for the performance of hospitals in each of the three priority areas for transformation: access to services, integration of services and optimal use of resources. The overall score or traffic light indicator is calculated by aggregating the score for the individual measures in each of these areas. For example, a high aggregate score in relation to resources is achieved by hospitals or services that are operating within their budget and have very low rates of absenteeism. The overall score or bar that we set to achieve a green light is very high for each of these areas. When HealthStat first began with the hospital system alone, none of the twenty-nine hospitals initially included achieved an overall green light for the three areas. We have now reached a point where seven of the hospitals now included have achieved this very high standard. In addition, progressive improvement in the overall scores has been seen in all but six of the thirty-four hospitals now included.

CHAPTER 14

Integrated Service Areas – A Structure to Manage Integrated Care

The Need for an Integrated Management Structure

An 84-year-old lady developed pneumonia and was referred to hospital where she was admitted on Monday afternoon. By Friday morning she was markedly improved, following three days of intravenous antibiotics. Her consultant agreed to discharge her home where she was to continue taking oral antibiotics. As she lived with her elderly husband she required some general care and nursing support for a few hours each day over the subsequent week. Unfortunately, it was not possible to provide such support at the weekend and so she had to remain in hospital. Over the course of the next week she became confused in hospital and ultimately had to be transferred to a nursing home. Her confusion worsened and she never returned home.

The alternative approach to her care, which as a result of the transformation programme is now available in several parts of the country, is through a community intervention team. Her GP, who made the diagnosis, refers her to the local hospital where she is assessed by a consultant at the medical assessment unit. She has a chest X-ray which confirms the diagnosis of pneumonia. Antibiotics are prescribed and a care plan drawn up. She is referred to the local community intervention team who assign a nurse to provide her with care at home in association with her GP. A home help assistant, who is part of the community intervention team, is assigned to provide support for household tasks in her home. Over the course of two weeks she has fully recovered and returns to leading a normal life at home.

Why did this lady ever have to be admitted to hospital, or if she had to be admitted why did she have to stay longer than was necessary? A major reason for this was that the Irish healthcare system was organised essentially as two separate businesses at the time of the establishment of the HSE. The two service pillars were the National Hospitals Office (NHO) and the Primary Community and Continuing Care services (PCCC). While it was clear that the NHO was responsible for all acute hospitals across the country, the PCCC pillar was responsible for a wide array of services, ranging from GP services to child protection and personal social services. People who worked for each service pillar had loyalty first and foremost to that pillar. Budgets and workforce were guarded jealously within each pillar. In the case of this elderly lady, the incentive was for community-based services to ensure that the high cost of providing care over the weekend remained a charge within the hospital budget and did not transfer to community services. There was nobody in a position to say that closing some hospital beds and using the resources to develop community intervention teams would be much better for patients and a better use of hospital and community funding. We were not providing optimal care but rather the best care that could be provided based on the dual service pillar structure of the healthcare system.

From the outset, we had to aim to integrate hospital and community services into a single service from the top of the organisation down to the provision of frontline services. Like many proposed changes, it may sound logical and seem straightforward to achieve, but the reality is different. From an organisational change perspective this presented a very significant challenge due to the fact that people had for many decades worked for either hospital or community services.

For example, physiotherapy departments in most hospitals were separate units to the physiotherapy services in the community in the same city or town. This had major implications for patients. A patient admitted with a stroke had their rehabilitation initiated in hospital by the physiotherapy department. However, when the patient was ready for discharge, the community-based physiotherapy team had to be contacted and had to agree to provide ongoing care for the patient. This involved a significant exchange of correspondence and other communications between the hospital physiotherapy services and the community-based services, which slowed the process of getting the patient home. More importantly, it was worrying for the patient and their family to be told that they were now moving from a group of therapists in whom they had a deep trust to a new group of therapists. This is overcome by having a single department for the geographic area, operating across the hospital and community. All therapists are then familiar with hospital and community treatment plans and would manage their patients using a standardised approach. This seamless transition is so important for patients and their families. A further benefit of this is that the therapists do not spend long periods of time writing reports for each other and organising the transfer of patients, as the patient is remaining under the care of their department.

The question again arises as to why dual structures were put in place for many clinical departments. It is clearly not in the interest of patients, but rather makes things more difficult for them. It is difficult to avoid the conclusion that such a structure evolved based on our requirements as professionals. It is important to point out that while physiotherapy is used in this example, the same applies to other services, including nursing, where public health nursing and hospital nursing departments are run as separate services.

There were notable exceptions. In a few locations across the country hospital and community departments were run as single departments. These included areas like Kerry and Galway where physiotherapy operated across the divide, and Kilkenny where dieticians and others formed single departments. I had the opportunity to meet a group of people in Galway who each had suffered a stroke and benefited from a physiotherapy service that was the same in the hospital and the community. They spoke of the immense relief it brought to them to know that they were remaining in the care of the same department as they moved home from hospital. Their stories reconfirmed for me the importance of bringing about an integrated healthcare service.

It was essential that we were able to present the case for moving to an integrated healthcare system as a change that was focused on improving care. We decided to prioritise advancing two objectives before making any structural changes: the development of primary care teams within community services (see Chapter 9) and the development of the clinical leadership programme (see Chapter 11). We hoped that if a team-based integrated approach began to be accepted as a better way of providing care that this would generate more support for the concept of integrating the management structure. Furthermore, if clinical leadership was developed to a significant degree, these leaders would hopefully identify the need for an integrated structure with single budgets across hospital and community services if optimal care was to be provided to people.

There was initially opposition to the integration of hospital and community services from both the Board of the HSE and the Department of Health and Children. The Department historically accounted to Government for healthcare in a defined way, based on measurement of the amount of services provided to the public. There has been little or no history of anybody reporting back to the Government on the quality of the patient experience. Running services in silos such as hospitals, and indeed in several silos or individual departments within communities, allows for easy counting of activity. Moving to establish an integrated healthcare system where our focus would be on improving the overall patient experience, rather than measuring individual points of encounter, would mean that the Department officials would have to convince the Government to use different outcome measures. For example, an effective integrated healthcare system results in patients leaving hospital much more quickly, after a hip replacement procedure. The length of time spent in hospital by such patients has halved in many Irish orthopaedic units. This is much better for the patient, but shows up as a reduction in the number of bed-days used in the hospital. Using the traditional measurement system, this makes the hospital appear less busy.

The Board of the HSE is ultimately the agent of the Department of Health and Children and the Government. In the absence of support from the Department, the Board adopted a sceptical view about the move to integrate our major service pillars. The organisational changes being proposed were radical, and the Board was concerned that such change could not be achieved while the organisation had to continue to run critical services on a day-to-day basis. Some took the view that you did not need to alter structures to implement an integrated approach to the provision of healthcare services. People with experience in other systems, especially in the private sector, expect that you can use 'work arounds' or, in other words, flexibility in work practices to ensure the services are provided in a seamless manner irrespective of the overall structure of the organisation. Unfortunately, getting people to operate in this way in a publicly provided system is much more difficult than proposing this type of flexibility in work practices in the private sector (see Chapter 15). It is therefore important in a public service environment to ensure that your organisation is structured in a way that supports the way you intend to provide services.

There was no single breakthrough point at which we managed to convince key stakeholders such as the Board and the Department about accepting a move to an integrated structure. What happened was that, at ground level in the organisation, more and more people who were beginning to work in teams became supportive of the need for integration because they wanted to provide services of the highest possible quality. Many clinical leaders across the different professional groups became strong advocates for this change. This support for change at the frontline ultimately resulted in an irrepressible demand for this change to occur. Managers and healthcare providers across the organisation began to speak more and more about the need for integration.

It was understandable that individuals on the HSE Board and in the Department were fearful that collapsing two huge structures, each with about 50,000 people working in them and each spending €5 billion annually, would be a huge risk for the organisation. This was an immense undertaking, requiring detailed planning to ensure that critical services were not undermined during the process. Nevertheless, we had to move quickly to achieve this. We appointed Laverne McGuinness, who was in charge of our PCCC services, to create the new Integrated Directorate to run all hospital and community services. She identified the many risks associated with a major integration of two almost separate businesses and developed a plan to manage the risks.

In addition to establishing a single integrated structure at the top of the organisation, four regional directors of operations were appointed, each covering a population of one million, to manage the provision of integrated services across four regions. These four directors were to promote the integration of services at the ground level in these regions.

Integrated Service Areas

Integrating the management of services under a single budget holder at the top of the organisation, or even for four regions of one million people each, was never on its own going to have a major impact on services provided at the frontline. Frontline services had to be integrated in a manner that was relevant to individual service providers and clients. We therefore proceeded to plan the development of integrated service areas. Integrated service areas were based on identifying all of the secondary care hospitals that were likely to continue to provide care in Ireland following our hospital reconfiguration programme and then mapping out the catchment areas for these hospitals. Each hospital would therefore be clear as to the precise population it was responsible for serving and the specific primary care teams that it was responsible to for providing high quality services in a timely manner. Similarly, the primary care teams, their clients and the population at large would be clear as to which hospital was responsible for providing their hospital services. An integrated service area hospital could in turn develop service level agreements with larger city-based hospitals for any advanced specialist services that were not available locally.

A healthcare delivery structure based on a single sustainable hospital and its catchment area is seen by professionals as being very relevant from a service delivery perspective. They can identify how the seamless movement of money and staff across the hospital–community divide in such areas can have an immediate impact on the quality of care that can be provided for their community. Integrated service areas are also critical in terms of being able to measure and manage performance in the delivery of services. With such a structure, it is clear who is accountable for the delivery of services and there is no confusion in terms of a number of hospitals providing the same services in the same area. The hospital is funded for and must accept responsibility for providing care for all patients from that area.

A challenge for us in planning integrated service areas on this basis was to justify the significant variation in the size of the population between areas. Because of the uneven distribution of population in Ireland the areas that have been established vary greatly in terms of their population. The smallest areas, for example Kerry or Sligo/Leitrim, have only approximately 100,000 people for community and hospital services, whereas other areas, such as the Mid-West or Galway/Roscommon, have a population of up to 350,000.

However, a structure based on a defined population requirement would, because of different population densities, result in services in disconnected areas being managed as a single unit. In healthcare delivery, you are, to a large degree, dependent on the commitment of your frontline professionals to manage their own performance in response to the needs of their community. Placing them in a structure that is based on population alone can undermine this as such a structure may be largely irrelevant in terms of the provision of healthcare services. This can also result in two or three secondary care hospitals operating within one unit, which creates a problem in measuring performance, because there can be confusion as to who is responsible for providing the service for an individual patient. Multiple hospital units operating within a single management structure may also devote a lot of their energy to competing with one another for resources within that structure. In contrast, when hospitals operate as single units in an integrated service area their performance in terms of providing timely service to their community is easily measured and their full focus is on improving the quality of their services.

The North West of Ireland is a good example of this. The combined population of Sligo, Leitrim and Donegal is only 230,000. There are two general hospitals, one in Sligo in the south of the area and one in the northern part in Letterkenny. For geographical reasons, these two hospitals are always likely to exist. It might appear logical to treat this whole area as one management unit; this was done in the past under the old Health Board Structure. Under such circumstances, each hospital competes for their share of the total resources allocated to that area. Arguments arise between the hospitals as to how large each catchment area is, and therefore how much resources they should get. Underperformance can be blamed on under-resourcing due to the ill-defined catchment populations. A sense of inequity in terms of resource distribution can undermine morale and performance in an institution.

In contrast, when Sligo and Letterkenny are in individual integrated service areas they are clear what their catchment area is, and which patients they are responsible for. They can focus on delivering the best possible services with the resources provided to them and performance can be accurately measured and compared to other integrated service areas. Their ambition to improve their performance incentivises the integration of their hospital and community services.

An integrated service area approach also allows for a very logical alignment of the senior manager for the area with the senior clinical leader or executive clinical director. Each is very clear as to their responsibilities and each can share easily in successes. Success is readily identified in such areas becasue they are built around a logical community base rather than a fixed population.

In 2010, the HSE initiated the rollout of integrated services areas along the western coast. My first experience of meeting an integrated services area management team was in Co. Kerry, which served 120,000 people and was responsible for community services and the acute hospital service based in Tralee. The enthusiasm of the management team for this new structure was incredible. The manager, Mr Michael Fitzgerald, and the clinical director, Mr Richard Liston, as well as all of their team, spoke of the fact that they now attended meetings focused on using their budget in the best way possible to improve services. They spoke about the old structure of hospital and community services where several meetings took place before a relatively simple decision was taken because everybody was concentrating on protecting their budget against the other service pillar.

It was always going to be easier to establish integrated service areas outside of Dublin because the hospital system and the community system were to a large degree owned by the State and managed by the HSE. In Dublin, all of the large hospitals are owned by the voluntary sector and operate through service level agreements with the HSE. Community services are either provided directly by the HSE or by other voluntary providers. Integrating services in Dublin as in the rest of the country involves establishing catchment areas for each of the Dublin hosptials. This has been done. Following this, agreement must be reached with the individual hospitals to take responsibility for community and hospital services in their catchment area. While discussions between the HSE and the voluntary hospital system began in 2010, this has not happened to date. It presents a significant challenge for all involved because the scope of community-based services in the Irish healthcare system is wide, including personal social services and child protection. Nevertheless, it will be difficult to establish an integrated approach to the provision of healthcare in Dublin unless full responsibility for all services in an area is under one management structure. While voluntary hospitals and their boards are understandably concerned about taking on this responsibility, there is a general sense that this is the right thing to do and some in the voluntary hospitals have begun to develop plans to undertake these responsibilities. It is likely to take a number of years before integrated service areas in Dublin are operational. Hopefully the benefits of an integrated approach in other areas will be a significant incentive to develop them in Dublin.

Developing an integrated approach to the provision of healthcare is a challenge internationally. Countries across the developed world are struggling with trying to establish systems that would make provision of care for patients as seamless as possible. Achieving this has been difficult, because it requires a marked change in how everyone in a healthcare system works. The experience in Ireland may ultimately be relevant to other countries.

The structural alterations at an administrative level, to support the delivery of integrated care, were not initiated in Ireland until the transformation programme was well under way. One is much more likely to succeed in gaining acceptance for an integrated management structure if professionals working at the frontline have already begun working in community-based teams and hospital-based clinicians have begun to identify the possibility of improving services by reaching out to work with these teams. Healthcare professionals at the frontline who have moved to providing service in a more integrated manner know that they need an integrated management structure to allow them to provide seamless integrated care. In our experience, clinical leaders quickly became very powerful advocates for integration once they began to see changes occurring on the ground. This bottom-up approach is a lot slower to develop than simply implementing a top-down approach to the integration of management structures. It is, however, essential if integration is to be seen as relevant by clinicians.

Chapter 15

Managing a Health Service in a Public Sector Environment

'Just Appoint a Real Manager'

One of the most frequent mantras recited in relation to improving performance in public services in general, but especially the health services, is that an experienced manager from the private sector should be appointed to manage the service as he or she would any other business. This straightforward view is regularly put forward on radio chat shows or in letters to the editors of newspapers. It all sounds so simple. As with all simple solutions, you have to ask the question as to why this has not yet happened in Ireland or other countries. In fact, it has been tried in other countries, most notably in the UK. However, the reality that managing in a public sector environment is very different to managing in the private sector soon becomes obvious.

The suggestion that successful managers in private sector enterprises could achieve similar success in a public sector enterprise is naive. It ignores the reality that the major shareholder for a public enterprise is the Government, and that governments will, if necessary, veto the executives' commercial decisions if these decisions have political consequences, which, especially in the health sector, is often the case. It also ignores the fact that many of the most powerful levers available to executives and managers in the private sector are not available to managers in public sector businesses.

These levers include the impact of customer satisfaction on the survival of an enterprise. If customers are not happy, it is highly unlikely that any private business venture would survive for a significant period of time. The fear of loss of competitiveness, failure to provide value for money or any potential loss of consumer confidence in the quality of services are major drivers of change in work practices in the private sector. Individuals who work in private sector companies know that any such failure may lead to the loss of their jobs or in bankruptcy and the loss of the entire company. Consumer satisfaction is often much less relevant in a public service environment because customer dissatisfaction with a service has limited consequences. In most public sector environments the risk of the overall enterprise failing is minimal. As a result, one of the major levers of change, consumer opinion, is generally not available or is certainly available to a much lesser degree to those who have to manage change in a public service environment.

A further challenge for public service managers is that centralised or national negotiation of contracts of employment disempowers local management, making it much more difficult for them to bring about positive change in the way services are provided. There is often little local accountability for the delivery of services to an acceptable level. Local managers, who are at the frontline managing service delivery, can become disillusioned because of the lack of sanctions they can apply if there is a marked level of underperformance by an individual or group.

Public service managers also have limited opportunities to use career advancement as a lever to incentivise change and improve performance among staff. A major incentive in the private sector is the individual's determination to gain promotion based on their performance. In contrast, in the public sector, promotion is often determined by length of service and, furthermore, once a senior position has been attained, an individual is extremely unlikely to be removed from that role, irrespective of performance.

In normal day-to-day commercial activities, it can be difficult for public sector managers to pursue the best possible outcome for the public in negotiating contracts. This is because there is no acknowledgement, reward or protection for individuals in the public service who take risks. In fact, the opposite may be the case. This can be exploited by the private sector in negotiating agreements or contracts with public servants. This was highlighted when the HSE began its renegotiation of contracts with the various parts of the pharmaceutical industry to reduce the cost of medication (see Chapter 12). The public servants from the HSE, who had the task of reducing the huge bill paid by Irish taxpayers for medicines, were severely criticised by the majority of politicians, who had been very successfully lobbied by the industry, despite the fact that they were seeking value for money for the taxpayer. People who are frustrated with the performance of public service managers should read Chapter 12 and the relevant transcripts of the meetings of the Oireachtas Joint Committee on Health and Children. They will provide insight into why it is so challenging to manage in a public service environment.

Performance management, which is central to improving the efficiency of private sector businesses, is much more difficult in a public service environment. It could be said that performance management as a term is an oxymoron in the context of a politically controlled public service. Politicians focus on achieving what is acceptable and not on what is best. Politics is ultimately about populism and management is very often the opposite of populism. The public service is asked to merge politics and excellent management. Clearly this is impossible. The public servant has to try to do the best he or she can in this environment, but the quality of service often suffers because of the understandable failure of the public servant to navigate this maze.

Committed public servants may be advised by colleagues to curb their enthusiasm and to understand that good ideas are not necessarily relevant or always welcomed in such an environment. While the political system demands that public servants should manage more effectively, it is perceived as naive if they seek to do this, which results in many potentially good managers becoming administrators. Ireland will have to achieve a wider separation between the political and executive arms of government if this issue is to be addressed.

Managing Healthcare Provision in the Public Sector

While there are major challenges to managing any public service effectively, there are additional challenges associated with managing health services in this environment. One way of assessing the impact of health sector specific issues on the capacity of managers to improve performance in the Irish health service is to consider how any other business would perform if it was managed under the same circumstances as the Irish health service. Let us for a moment consider that the largest supermarket in each major town is owned by the Government and all of the staff are employed by the Government. Your taxes pay for your food and therefore you do not have to pay the supermarket for your grocery supplies each week.

There is a manager for the supermarket but the individual departments have discretion in deciding what goods are supplied to you, which can't be challenged by the supermarket manager. The head of the meat counter decides how much meat you get and the head of the fruit and vegetable counter decides how much fruit you get. They also decide how quickly you get your supplies. Each of these department heads is a permanent and pensionable employee of the State, but, despite this, also works for a smaller privately owned supermarket across the road which operates on a cash basis.

You, the customer, are dependent on these grocery supplies and therefore you are extremely thankful to the people working in each department when they provide them to you, even after a long wait. Your appreciation is such that you are hesitant to ask why they operate the supermarket in this manner. Meanwhile, many others wait outside the supermarket in long lines hoping to be served. Rather than complain when they reach the fruit and vegetable counter, they are also extremely grateful to the staff for what they get. Those who have money avoid the long line by moving their business to the privately owned supermarket across the road.

Could I be serious in suggesting that the structure of this supermarket can be used to explain why health services are sometimes administered, rather than managed? There are many factors specific to the provision of health services which make this supermarket analogy appropriate. These include:

1. The Provider, Not the Consumer, Determines Demand

This is a major reason why healthcare provision and, therefore, its management are so different to any other business. In almost every other business or service, the consumer or customer determines the demand for that service. However, in healthcare, the professional provider, generally a doctor, determines for the most part what services, and how much of each service, will be provided to a patient (see Chapter 11). This presents a major challenge for those who manage resources and those who attempt to bring about improvements in patient management pathways.

2. The Provider Determines the Rate of Supply of Services

Patients will generally attend where and when the provider, usually a clinician, determines. The number of patients seen over a fixed period of time is also largely determined by the provider, based on their clinical automomy. Ultimately, any service, not just a health service, that cannot be held accountable for the promptness or pace of service delivery is likely to become inefficient. In a public health service, the acceptance that the provider determines the pace of service delivery and that the consumer should wait patiently for a service can become the culture (see Chapters 11 and 13).

3. Absence of Hierarchy among Medical Professionals

Prior to the introduction of the clinical leadership programme by the HSE (Chapter 11), most senior doctors in Ireland operated in an environment where there was no hierarchical structure. Managing change or improving performance among professionals who each have the authority to operate independently is very difficult and in many instances, if the professional chooses to operate independently, is impossible.

4. The Consumer Is Vulnerable and Dependent on the Provider

An individual seeking a healthcare service is often worried and glad of any help they receive in identifying the cause of their symptoms and providing cure or relief. With a publicly provided health service the consumer often does not see themselves as paying for this service and as therefore being deserving of it in the same way as they do with other services that they pay for. Also, healthcare professionals, because they exercise considerable influence over life and death decisions, may see themselves as being a critical support for, rather than a service provider to, a patient. This is the opposite of what pertains in almost any other service where the provider is dependent on the consumer for their custom.

As a result of the imbalance in the customer–provider relationship, any underperformance by the professional is rarely questioned by the service user. The customer (or patient) is vulnerable and the professional usually gets positive affirmation of their performance. Blame for any problems with service delivery is usually apportioned by the patient to management or other individuals not directly involved in their care. Under such circumstances, it is difficult for professionals to identify the way that they practice as having anything but a positive impact on patients. There is, therefore, little stimulus for professionals to change the processes through which care is provided, to focus on improving the patient journey – in other words, to do things differently and more effectively.

So, if I was to inform the highly successful CEO of a major supermarket chain tomorrow that, henceforth, staff in each section of his shops would be allowed to determine how much food would be supplied to each customer and when it would be supplied, how would he react? Furthermore, the heads of the various departments in his shops could, in future, also work for a different shop across the road where they would be paid for providing services to any customers who left the queues outside his supermarket. Finally, all of the staff are given permanent public service contracts. Would this manager be in a position under the changed circumstances to continue to manage the shop as successfully as before?

Obviously healthcare is a much more complex and high-risk business than running a supermarket. There are good reasons why professionals need to have significant autonomy in terms of providing services for individual patients. Nevertheless, this comparison demonstrates how much more difficult it is to manage performance in a health service environment. This may help explain why all of the problems that affect the provision of health services across the world have not been solved by simply moving management experts in from other sectors to run health services.

Chapter 16

Governance in Ireland and Its Effect on Healthcare

There has been much discussion recently on corporate governance in the banking system. Governance of the health service is also of vital importance. The quality of health service governance systems ultimately determines the quality of care provided to patients.

I have always found 'governance', as a term, confusing and I suspect that many of us use different interpretations depending on the context. I have, therefore, taken the liberty of including definitions from two dictionaries:

The Webster Collegiate Dictionary defines governance as 'exercise of authority; control; government'.

The Oxford English Dictionary defines it as 'the action or manner of governing a state, organisation, etc.'

The principles of good governance are similar across all sectors. However, there are specific features in healthcare, and especially healthcare which is publicly provided, that are particularly challenging in terms of ensuring good governance.

Challenges to Governance in Healthcare

Good governance ensures that services provided are of the highest quality and that they are provided in the most efficient and fair manner possible. To achieve this, the board and senior management of a health service provider need regular reports on the outcomes for patients. They also need performance measures which evaluate the efficiency of the services provided, including an analysis of the costs associated with treating various groups of patients. Historically, however, there has been very little or no measurement of the performance of institutions, clinical departments or individual clinicians in Ireland, either in terms of the safety or quality of care provided or the efficiency of the provider system. Many boards and management teams have therefore had to operate without the critical information that they require for them to exercise their responsibilities. The establishment and ongoing development of HealthStat is beginning to address this deficit at national level (see Chapter 13).

A further difficulty for boards in exercising their responsibilities is the low level of external clinical representation on such boards. Without clinical experts who are independent of the institution or body itself it is difficult for a board to critically evaluate performance in a healthcare setting. The board can find itself in a situation where its capacity to evaluate the quality of services in the institution is almost totally dependent on the input of the institution's own clinicians.

Even institutions with strong governance structures often struggled to have a positive impact on how services were provided because senior clinicians traditionally operated outside any hierarchical structure with little or no reporting relationship within the organisation. The development of the clinical leadership programme, with the appointment of clinical directors to whom consultants report, should greatly enhance the capacity of boards and senior management to ensure that more appropriate governance operates across their organisation (see Chapters 10 and 11).

Healthcare is relatively unique in that a single adverse event may have a huge impact on an organisation. A healthcare organisation may carry out 50,000 procedures, but if one of these procedures is mishandled the entire organisation faces an immediate public demand to address the adverse event. This is understandable because of the immense consequences that can attach to such an incident for the patient and their family. Unfortunately, in healthcare, the reputational damage associated with an adverse incident does not always promote an improvement in the provision of care in general. This is because the entire effort of the organisation may be focused on dealing with the incident, rather than on the governance or organisational factors that can underlie such incidents.

Implementing good governance in health and social care services can also be difficult in a situation where professionals exert a major impact on public opinion through the media. Boards and managers may find it difficult to challenge the performance of groups or individuals who use the media to portray themselves as defending the best interests of patients in battles with a bureaucracy, while depicting management as uncaring and focused only on cost control. It is difficult for boards and management to demand improved performance under circumstances where the professional's account is rarely, if ever, challenged by the media.

Responsibilities of Board Members in the Health Service

Corporate governance structures in healthcare vary from national organisations such as the HSE and large national voluntary bodies to more local structures such as the boards of individual voluntary hospitals or voluntary providers of community-based services like disability services.

Who does a board member on a public body represent? This is a question that we should all ask if we find ourselves in such a position. The answer is not as straightforward as we may think it is. If I am a member of a national governance structure in any public sector, for example the ESB, CIE or HSE, who is my major stakeholder? In whose interests am I making decisions? Is it my responsibility to represent what is in the best interests of the public or am I first and foremost responsible for making decisions based on the requirements of the minister or government who appointed me?

People may immediately come to the conclusion that the two stakeholders, the public and the Government, are the same. This assumption may underlie problems that have arisen in the past with corporate governance in the public sector. The Government's requirement is often to achieve a compromise between the optimal solution and what is required to maintain electoral support, or the support of some powerful commercial or professional groups. From a political perspective, it is not always in the Government's interest to obtain the best possible value for money or to have services reorganised in the safest possible way, because trying to achieve these goals might result in public relations campaigns which have adverse electoral consequences for the Government. A board member operating in the public interest should be responsible for challenging decisions that are not in the public interest but by doing so may immediately place themselves in conflict with the government and minister who appointed them.

Understanding this paradox is critical to understanding the risks that exist for board members of public bodies and public servants attempting to do the right thing. Governments consistently demand in public that public agencies and public servants must manage the delivery of services more effectively. Politicians love to be heard demanding better performance from public servants. However, the agency or public servant who responds to this request and demands improved performance from staff and better contractual agreements with suppliers may quickly find themselves in conflict with the Government. In truth, what politicians and often governments want is that the system is managed, but not too effectively. As I stated earlier, performance management in a public sector environment is to a degree an oxymoron. Public agencies and public servants are ultimately required to manage to a level that achieves what is acceptable rather than what is optimal.

An example of this is where politicians were and are constantly calling for a reduction in the administrative staff in the HSE. In 2009, the management of the HSE proposed centralising the issuing of medical cards to the public. The medical card allows free access to all health services to individuals with an income below a certain threshold. Historically, the determination of who is entitled to a medical card has been made in local health offices across the country. By standardising the eligibility requirements and centralising the process surrounding the issuing of these cards the HSE could reduce the number of administrative staff required to support the process from 434 to 150. A centralised service also provides quicker turnaround times in terms of issuing medical cards to clients. It means that, if families wish, they can submit their application electronically and have the medical card issued within three weeks, compared to an average wait of three months in the past. When this new process was initiated, there was an outcry from politicians across the political spectrum.

It was difficult to believe that the HSE was being critisised in the Dáil for improving the efficiency of issuing medical cards while at the same time reducing the number of administrative staff. However, standardising the process and issuing medical cards from a national centre removed the opportunity for politicians to exert any influence over the issuing of these valuable cards to constituents. Politicians wanted less administrators but not if this removed the politicians' capacity to influence the process, or reduced the number of administrative staff in their local area.

For the brave board member who decides to act in the public interest irrespective of the political risks there is another potential landmine. What is in the public interest nationally and what the public demand in a specific region may be very different. The public demand may be strongly influenced by parochial factors. A good example of this is the reconfiguration of hospitals where, at its broadest level, the public understand the need for hospitals to be large enough to maintain the expertise of the workforce and support this concept at a national level. However, the public response is generally very different when their local hospital is affected. This is understandable as change like this is often seen as an attack on a local community or as favouring one area over another. This was seen in the response to our plans to build one major hospital in place of the five existing hospitals in the north-eastern region of Ireland. Almost everybody from the different areas were in support of this concept but this unanimous support evaporated when the site for this single hospital was chosen (see Chapter 7).

This type of response is not unique to the health service. How does a CIE board member respond to a plan to reopen a disused railway line in a rural part of Ireland? Is the interest of the Irish people better served by such an investment as compared to investment in transport infrastructure elsewhere in the country? If it is not, how does that board member oppose such a decision when it has, for local political reasons, the full support of the minister and government who appointed him or her?

Because of this conflict, it is essential for good governance that the responsibilities of public sector board members are clear and unambiguous. Is it the duty of board members to represent the public interest, or is it to do what is expedient in terms of other key stakeholders, including a government's political requirements? If it is the latter then good governance is impossible. However, be careful what you wish for! If we want board members to act in the public interest, and not that of the government of the day or other powerful stakeholders, we need to understand the consequences that flow from this as it is likely to result in a major reconfiguration of public services in Ireland.

The governance of institutions such as voluntary hospitals or other voluntary agencies in the healthcare sector is also very important. As a board member of a voluntary hospital or similar structure, am I responsible to the institution or to the public? In the commercial or for-profit private sector there is no such conflict. A board member of such a private sector company has a responsibility to maximise the performance of the company for its shareholders and to promote its standing in public. In contrast, the board member of a voluntary agency which is almost fully funded by the public has a potentially serious conflict to deal with. For example, when a decision is made to initiate a new clinical service, is that decision based on what is best from the point of view of providing services to the public at large, or on what will improve the institution's standing?

It may be difficult for the members of such boards to be certain of whether they are acting in the best interests of the public or of the institution. The answer to a simple question might give some indication. Has anybody on a hospital board ever proposed that a service provided by that hospital be discontinued and moved to another hospital? If not, it is difficult to believe that the public interest has priority over the interests of institutions.

Cultural Issues and Governance: Consensus

There may be cultural issues in Ireland that affect us in achieving good governance in our public services. Leadership and good governance are often poor bedfellows with popularity. We, as a people, are generally collegial in our interactions; straightforward assertiveness is not something that we commonly practice. A disagreement in relation to a decision is often considered to be a personal argument rather than simply a professional difference of opinion. These characteristics can result in a belief that consensus on a decision indicates that the decision is a good one. This is dangerous because, as has often been stated, consensus may simply indicate that the easier decision was taken rather than facing up to the more difficult decision.

The basis on which I make these comments can justifiably be questioned. I believe, however, that there is evidence to support this opinion. Many public service boards in Ireland would confirm that they rarely hold a vote on decisions, even major decisions. In fact, it can be a significant source of pride that they seldom require a vote to reach a decision. I would suggest that taking important decisions without holding a vote should be seen as a failure in terms of good governance. A culture based on the absence of votes at board level being a positive thing is a culture that promotes consensus, inhibiting constructive discussion and argument around decisions.

Further evidence is the pride that is displayed by boards in decisions being unanimous when votes are taken. Unanimous decisions are seen as indicating that the board is operating well, which confirms our tendency as a society to be collegial and to avoid asking challenging questions. Perhaps even more damaging is the fact that when a vote does take place the chairperson may request dissenting board members to agree to a decision becoming unanimous. The message to the dissenters is clear: holding an alternative view is not something that is encouraged. Group thinking is thereby encouraged. This is not likely to be unique to the health sector. For example, indications are that banking organisations operated in such a manner in the creation of the property bubble and their own subsequent collapse.

Can We Improve Governance in Irish Healthcare?

A number of recent developments will help to improve governance in the health sector. The introduction of a performance measurement and management system with the establishment of HealthStat by the HSE (see Chapter 13) supports good governance. Similarly, the clinical leadership programme (see Chapter 11) is a significant contributor.

As in other sectors, the way that members are appointed to boards in healthcare is important for good governance. We need a systematic approach to how we choose board members. Board members should be selected based on their competency following an open application procedure. Every citizen in the country should have the right to apply to serve on public sector boards and it should not be difficult for citizens to exercise this right. This is essential if we are to move away from situations where existing members recommend the appointment of a new member. We must avoid personal friendships and acquaintances as the basis for appointing board members if we are to reduce the risk of group thinking.

Boards should be encouraged to have votes on all major decisions. An absence of votes should be seen as an indication of poor governance rather than the successful functioning of a board. Similarly, unanimous decisions should not be the Holy Grail. In fact, concern should be raised in a situation where most decisions are unanimous. There should be formal documentation as to why the board overruled a dissenting opinion. This does not need to be a complex bureaucratic process. All that is required is for the board to indicate why the dissenting opinion was not considered to serve the public interest better than the decision they endorsed. The requirement to outline why the decision made was in the best interest of the public compared to the dissenting proposal would also support board members in fulfilling their responsibilities to the public when the government which appointed them might be advocating a different decision.

The majority of people who sit on public boards want to do the right thing for the public. We need to support them in achieving this by addressing the challenges outlined above. There is, at the present time in Ireland, a major interest in how we can improve governance in general. This presents an opportunity for organisation in the healthcare area to implement changes that can ensure not only improved governance, but an associated ongoing improvement in the quality and efficiency of our health services.

Conclusion

There will be many, who, having looked at the title of this book, will be surprised at a suggestion that patients are not put first in determining how we run our healthcare service. This will include many professionals who work in healthcare, as well as the public at large. Having read this book, I hope some people will start to question why healthcare systems around the world have been established and run in the way they are. It is important to remember the often stated adage that systems are perfectly designed to produce the outcomes they do. The challenge of redesigning the healthcare system and implementing changes that ensure services are provided in a way that makes things as easy as possible for patients is not unique to Ireland. The development of an integrated healthcare system, which provides care in the right place and in as seamless a manner as possible to the public, is, as yet, only an aspiration in most countries.

Providers did not intentionally set out to design the health service in a way that is far from ideal for patients. Historically, most healthcare services were either provided directly by or under the direction of doctors. As more elaborate and comprehensive services were developed, and with the appointment of many other professionals, such as specialist nurses, physiotherapists, social workers, speech and language therapists, occupational therapists, and others, each group developed its service model, which was similar to that of doctors, that is, they operated as independent professional groups.

People may argue that the analogies used in this book – the operation of a hotel (Chapter 1) and a supermarket (Chapter 15) – to illustrate how irrational many of the processes are that underlie the provision of healthcare are simplistic, considering the complexity of some healthcare services. However, other complex and high-risk industries, such as the airline industry or the nuclear-power industry, are known to be very amenable to change, especially change focused on improving quality and effectiveness. The example of the airline industry's success in implementing change to improve safety is regularly used to encourage professionals in the healthcare arena to adopt change to improve the quality of care we provide. Despite this, healthcare systems are recognised internationally as being the most resistant to change. Jacky Jones, in her *Irish Times* healthcare commentary on 12 April 2011, speculated as to why differences between systems might exist. She pointed out that pilots are the first to arrive at the crash site and, of course, nuclear plant workers are likely to be the first exposed to radiation leaks. They, therefore, have a vested interest in adopting any change which will improve safety and save lives.

In 2005, when the HSE was established, most people accepted that there were major problems with how the health services operated. Since 1997, there had been a dramatic increase in spending on healthcare, with the Exchequer allocation increasing from €3.6 billion in 1997 to €7 billion in 2001. By 2005, expenditure was €11.5 billion. Most of this increased investment was accounted for by an increase in the number of staff, pay increases and increases in payments for various drug schemes.

Considering that significant problems continued to exist in the health service in 2005, despite a marked increase in expenditure over the previous eight years, the proposed solution to the problems was surprising. In 2005, all of the major stakeholders, including doctors and nurses, the political parties and the public, were committed to further increasing expenditure to expand the same healthcare delivery system.

In 2005, when the HSE decided that major reform of the way health services were provided was required, we were placing ourselves at a fork in the road. The road to the right, level and paved, was one on which we could have easily travelled as we continued to expand the existing system. The HSE would simply demand more money to do more of the same and could blame all failings on the fact that we did not get enough money from the taxpayer. This would remove any responsibility from the HSE, as the provider of services, and place all the blame on Government. We would demand money to build the proposed 3,000 extra beds, which would require 12,000 more staff and increase our annual day-to-day spending by over a €1 billion each year. This expanding system would insist that patients in Ireland continued to be admitted to hospital far more often and stay longer than in comparable countries, and pay more for their medication than patients in the rest of Europe. Ironically, this approach would have made the new organisation popular with most of the professionals and representative groups who were commenting publicly on the HSE in 2005.

Albert Einstein once said that we cannot solve our problems with the same thinking that we used when we created them. It was imperative that we considered going left at the fork in the road. Unfortunately, this road was going to be uphill, unpaved and potholed, and with plenty of dangerous bends to negotiate. Laying the foundations for an integrated healthcare system would be a difficult journey. We would not be building more hospital beds. We would plan to have more services provided by teams of professionals working on new community-based primary care teams. Patients would be able to receive physiotherapy, occupational therapy, counselling or dietetic advice without having to go to hospital. If you needed an urgent specialist opinion, the hospital would provide rapid access through medical and surgical assessment units, where you could get immediate access to a senior clinician without having to be admitted to hospital. You would also have access to diagnostic services through such units. If you needed surgery or other treatment, if possible this would be provided as a day procedure without the need for you to stay in hospital overnight. If you did require admission to hospital for a number of days, you would be facilitated by being admitted on the morning of your procedure, rather than a few days in advance. If you developed a chronic disease, such as diabetes or high blood pressure, your treatment would be co-ordinated by a key worker on your primary care team in the community, who would also liaise with the hospital services, thus ensuring the implementation of standardised treatment plans. Your hospital would be a comprehensive centre capable of providing the highest quality of care, based on having an adequate workload to maintain all of the skills required, especially in critical areas such as intensive care, cardiac care, cancer treatment and surgical interventions. All facets of your care would be measured and managed in a transparent way, allowing comparison with similar units in different parts of the country.

When you consider the choices that had to be made at this fork in the road, you might think that choosing the more progressive road would have been quite easy. It would surely have been more appropriate to follow the direction that would have provided the best service for the public. But almost everybody wanted to continue along the comfortable paved route. Why?

For those of us who work in the health system – doctors, nurses and managers – increasing our numbers while allowing us to continue on the same road was always going to be a much more attractive option. Politicians also liked this approach as it would keep all local hospitals open; in fact, it would possibly increase the size of many hospitals and bring about more local employment. The public should have been the group to demand a new direction, but in healthcare the public find it very difficult to challenge those of us who, as professionals, provide them with essential services.

Travelling uphill on the unpaved road meant asking health professionals and others in the new organisation to undertake major change in terms of how they worked. Moving to working in multidisciplinary teams in communities, thereby creating a single point of access for patients to all the services they require, places professionals in a position where they have to respond to demands from the public almost immediately. Similarly, having to provide immediate access for patients to services through medical and surgical assessment units dramatically changes the way hospital-based professionals have to work. You are essentially being asked to work in the same way as people do in every other service industry – by making yourself available on demand to those who pay for the service. It is not surprising that change of this nature is slow.

This challenge faced by many leaders in the HSE, both managers and clinicians who were committed to implementing change, is neatly encapsulated in the following quotation on reform:

> And it ought to be remembered that there is nothing more difficult to take in hand, more perilous to conduct, or more uncertain in its success, than to take the lead in the introduction of a new order of things. Because the innovator has for enemies all those who have done well under the old conditions, and lukewarm defenders in those who may do well under the new. This coolness arises partly from fear of the opponents, who have the laws on their side, and partly from the incredulity of men, who do not readily believe in new things until they have had a long experience of them.

This quotation appears in Chapter 6 of *The Prince* by Niccolò Machiavelli, written in the sixteenth century. It remains particularly apt in the context of reforming a publicly funded healthcare system in the twenty-first century. It is very difficult to reform a healthcare service if the public who pay for the service, and who will benefit from the changes, do not feel that they are in a position to insist on change from those of us who provide their frontline services.

I hope that this book will have convinced readers that healthcare services will only provide the best possible care for the public when clinicians across all professional groups assume leadership roles in establishing a patient-focused service. When the health service is under-performing or major mistakes are made, the public and the professionals who provide services have in the past regularly blamed the system. But do doctors, nurses and other healthcare professionals not themselves constitute the system?

The Oxford English Dictionary defines system as 'a set of connected things or parts that form a whole or work together'. In healthcare, this would suggest that those of us who are healthcare professionals are, to a large extent, the system. When we blame the system, we are in essence blaming ourselves. The healthcare system can only be accountable when the public and we, as professionals, accept this. The alternative is for all of us to take the easy approach by demanding solutions to problems with a system from which we have excluded ourselves. Ultimately this means that nobody is accountable.

This book will have made a significant contribution if more clinicians accept the need to assume leadership roles. As clinicians or other professionals, it is our responsibility to ensure that services are improved for everyone, and not just our individual patients. Leadership is part of being a clinician. Unfortunately, leadership is often mistakenly associated with those who stand in front of their colleagues and reassure them that all of the problems are caused by other people and by the ubiquitous system.

In contrast, good clinical leaders are people who, having identified the problem, outline a vision of where we need to go. Most importantly, they have the courage to lead people on that journey. There are many clinicians who have already taken up this challenge as part of the development of clinical leadership within the healthcare transformation programme. It is a remarkable change to see dedicated professionals willing to take responsibility for bringing about changes that are often not popular, because they are committed to improving services for the public. This is radically different to what happened in the pre-HSE era, when healthcare professionals generally sat on the outside feeling disenfranchised and unable to see an opportunity to contribute to change.

Reform – Has anything Been Achieved?

In the preface I considered Arthur Schopenhauer's contention that every truth passes through three stages: first it is ridiculed; then it is opposed; and finally it is regarded as self-evident.

I believe it is fair to say that the Irish healthcare transformation plan has passed through all of the stages described by Schopenhauer. When the HSE stated in 2005 that the way forward for the Irish health service was not to build more hospital beds, as planned at that stage by both the Government and opposition parties, but rather to invest in developing an integrated healthcare system, it was certainly ridiculed. Clinicians who were media commentators and leaders of professional representative bodies in the health sector regularly stated that a small number of people in the HSE were the only people in the country who believed that we did not require these new hospital beds to solve the problems facing our health system. Every political party included a commitment to building thousands more hospital beds in their general election manifestos in 2007. However, now, in the second half of 2011, government ministers and almost all media commentators, as well as many healthcare professionals, are outlining the need to continue to make our hospitals more efficient and to deliver far more of our health services through community-based structures. Not alone in Ireland, but across many countries in Europe and in the US, the demand is now for the development of integrated healthcare services. The UK Prime Minister David Cameron constantly refers to the need for integration in reforming the British National Health Service.

The good news is that we are finally travelling in the right direction, rather than speeding along a wrong road. Most people now regard the need to continue to develop an integrated healthcare system as self-evident. However, understandably, people want to see progress at a much faster pace.

How far along the road have we travelled? The process is well underway, with the most difficult part – the acceptance of the need to change the way we work as professionals – now accepted by the majority. We now have a majority of healthcare professionals in communities across Ireland working as part of teams. These teams are at different stages of development, but with every passing year their maturation greatly improves their capacity to provide excellent services to the communities they serve. They require new infrastructure to achieve their optimal potential and, again, while excellent infrastructure has been developed in some locations, in the current economic climate it is going to be a number of years before the new centres are available in all communities.

There are community intervention teams in place which allow people, especially the elderly, to be treated during an acute illness in their own homes. We need many more and we have to continue to focus on moving resources from hospitals to support the development of such teams.

Our hospitals are also undergoing major change in terms of how people work within them. There is a new acceptance that it is the responsibility of clinicians to ensure that patients are only admitted if there is no alternative. Medical and surgical assessment units that involve a whole new way of providing services for hospital-based professionals are established in many hospitals, and they are central to facilitating patients who are receiving the majority of their care without requiring admission to hospital.

There is also an acceptance that many of our smaller hospitals cannot safely maintain comprehensive 24-hour services, and hospital reconfiguration, which previously was considered impossible to achieve, is now accepted by most healthcare professionals as essential if we are to provide high quality services. Reconfiguration is well advanced in a number of areas across the country. The building of a state-of-the-art children's hospital in Dublin will hopefully proceed, but it would never be possible if we had invested huge resources in rebuilding the existing children's hospitals as a solution to our problem.

Reconfiguration of hospital services has been linked to remarkable changes in the ambulance service. Advanced paramedics are now providing life-saving interventions at the site of emergencies, interventions which traditionally were considered impossible to provide if a doctor was not present.

Our cancer services for women with breast cancer are now among the best in Europe, thanks to the wonderful leadership shown by Professor Tom Keane. We may never again be able to make the large investment associated with developing this specialised cancer service, but Professor Susan O'Reilly, who is now the HSE national director for cancer services, is a superb clinical leader. I am certain she will continue to markedly improve services for all other cancer patients.

While there has been much criticism about the pace of implementation of the Vision for Change programme for mental health services, significant progress has been made in transforming the mental health services as a result of great leadership shown by clinicians, including some inspirational mental health nurses who took up the challenge of planning and implementing radical changes in their own areas. Implementing the Vision for Change in mental health services is, in the present economic environment, slower than planned, but the critical issue is, as with the reconfiguration of hospital services and primary care teams, that we continue on this road of change.

The new consultant contract is central to developing an integrated healthcare system. The contractual arrangements for consultants prior to the transformation programme, whereby consultants could work in both public and private hospitals, could never be consistent with developing an integrated healthcare system focused on providing seamless access to care for the public. As a result of the new contract, over the next ten years the Irish private hospital system will evolve and operate separately to the public hospital system. This will be much better for all involved, removing many potential conflicts of interest.

We now have acceptance among healthcare and other professionals that our performance has to be constantly measured, and that such measures should be used to identify where improvements have to be made. This represents a sea change. Who in 2005 would have believed that we would have a range of performance measures, relating to how we provide individual services in hospitals and in communities across Ireland, publically available on the HSE website (www.hse.ie/eng/staff/HealthStat)? The practical gains of performance assessment and subsequent change in processes are seen in areas like child and adolescent psychiatry, where waiting times for children and families decreased dramatically as a result of the changes led by a lead clinician, Dr Brendan Doody. Again,

HealthStat must continue to evolve and develop outcome measures which more accurately reflect the quality of our services. As with the rest of the transformation programme, persistence and patience will be required. Consistent with Schopenhauer's statement, the requirement for performance measurement and management is now accepted by most as being self-evident.

There is now also acceptance that managing the Irish healthcare system is about more than simply providing clinical services, but that there is also a responsibility on us all to ensure far better value for money for taxpayers in terms of expenditure on health services. The achievements of HSE staff working in business functions such as finance, procurement, estates management and human resources are never seen by the public, despite the savings they have delivered and the efficiency they have demonstrated in completing major projects on time. The Irish health service had traditionally overrun budgets. During the period 2005–2010, the HSE consistently delivered more than the planned volume of services each year and stayed within budget. This is a remarkable achievement in a health sector environment, and yet these are the back office people who are so readily criticised whenever the health service is discussed.

The HSE adopted a much more rigorous approach to contractual negotiations. This contrasts sharply with what pertained prior to 2005, when many of the contractual agreements in place could certainly only be described as being hugely beneficial to the suppliers rather than to the taxpayer. Better value for money is now being achieved through far more robust contractual relationships in high expenditure areas, from pharmaceutical supplies to the provision of local office supplies. There is still much to be done in developing national financial control and information technology systems. Again, it would be wonderful if all of this could be achieved more quickly.

The Huge Cost of Our Failures

While this is a book focused on transformation and change, unfortunately you could also write several books on the many tragedies that occurred relating to people using our healthcare services from 2005 to 2010. Healthcare is a remarkably difficult area to work in because even one error may have calamitous consequences – a person may die or be permanently damaged by a single error. There is no escaping the fact that errors will occur in every healthcare system in the world, but we have to ensure that these are minimised because of the consequences for individuals and their families. There were many occasions over the past five years when we made errors that had terrible consequences. These incidents ranged from people not having cancer correctly diagnosed to our failure to adequately protect children who were in contact with our child protection services.

Transformation programmes in healthcare can be undermined by serious incidents that occur during the years of change. Devastating incidents, in terms of their effects on individuals or families, resulting from failings of the healthcare system, undermine public confidence in the system as a whole. When major incidents occur, politicians and others constantly call for people to stop changing and to simply manage the existing processes well. Paradoxically, therefore, the changes required to try to ensure that incidents are less likely to recur can be stalled by the incidents themselves.

I can only hope that individuals and their families who have suffered because of errors made by us in the health services will see the transformation programme as a genuine attempt to improve the quality of care we provide, thereby reducing the risk of serious incidents reccurring. In Canada, it has been estimated that up to 10,000 people die every year as a result of preventable adverse incidents associated with the provision of medical care. In Holland, the estimate is that up to 2,000 people per year die as a result of such incidents. This varies from misdiagnosis to the wrong medication being administered and fatal errors being made during surgical procedures. While the estimates are relatively crude, because of the difficulty of making such assessments, there is no reason to believe that the level of preventable deaths that occur in the Irish health care system is proportionately different. Change programmes such as the transformation programme are essential if we are to reduce these tragic occurrences to a minimum.

We struggled in our attempts to reform the way in which childcare services were provided. There is no denying that the HSE was, from the beginning, very challenged by the breadth of its responsibilities, which included child and personal social services. I would be the first to accept that a comprehensive health and personal social services structure for delivering services, is ideal, but it is very challenging to achieve. Acute healthcare services, both in hospitals and the community, are almost always going to be prioritised ahead of other services. Child protection services are of immense importance and cannot be managed simply as an add-on to the health service. Despite aspiring to the ideal in terms of a comprehensive system, the practical reality is that these services will only receive the detailed attention they require in an environment where everybody is not distracted by the daily challenges facing the health service.

What Does the Future Hold?

Can the transformation programme be sustained? Yes, but only if the public and clinical leaders ensure that we continue to go in the right direction. The public must realise that they pay for the health service in the same way as they do for other services. They must demand accountability from each of us professionals, in terms of providing high quality services, and must insist on the most seamless possible system for providing care, just as they would when staying in a hotel. Professionals have to accept that models of care have to change dramatically in the new healthcare system and that they are ultimately responsible for how well or not the system performs. Clinical leaders have to continue to step forward and lead the changes that will ensure services are provided in a comprehensive manner by teams of professionals.

The *New England Journal of Medicine* published an article in June 2011 on what they referred to as the significant overcrowding and long waits on trolleys that exist in emergency rooms across the US. In this, Drs Kellermann and Martinez express their view that healthcare in the US has to change radically. They refer to two competing views of the future: 'one, driven by deteriorating access to care, is a future where primary care is unavailable, specialty care is unaffordable, and no one answers the phone after 4.00 p.m.' They go on to say:

> The alternative view is much brighter. It's a future where healthcare is centered on the needs of patients, not the convenience of providers. Health information flows regularly and securely from the patient's home to his or her doctor's office, the emergency department or the hospital whenever and wherever it is needed. Thanks to teamwork and a powerful commitment to safety, care transitions are seamless and risk free. As a

> result, patients consistently get the right care at the right time in the right place. (2001: 2278–2279)

While the provision of healthcare in the US is different in many respects to Ireland, the sentiments outlined by Drs Kellermann and Martinez are very pertinent here. They are essentially describing our transformation programme – the provision of integrated care based on teamwork, professionals radically altering the way they work and putting the patient before the provider. Most healthcare systems across the world will have to commence this journey of change if they are to be sustainable.

The greatest risk to ongoing transformation towards an integrated healthcare system in Ireland is the re-emergence of 'quick-fix' approaches to improving health services. Quick-fix propositions are attractive to everyone, including the public, who are often frustrated by the slow pace of sustainable change. People with experience in healthcare and in other industries know that quick fixes do not lead to sustainable change. If they worked, companies across the world would have used them rather than investing enormous effort in major change programmes which demand years of commitment. Unfortunately, quick fixes are very popular with politicians. This is understandable as their political survival is often dependent on rapid changes in services. This may, however, explain why so many health services struggle to achieve their optimal potential.

An integrated health system would ideally be supported by the way we pay for healthcare. Changing to integrated healthcare services will require a radical change for many countries in the way they fund healthcare, especially in the US and other insurance-based systems. These are likely to progress from a system in which a fee is paid for each service to a payment system based on coverage of the whole population. Insurance systems based on a fee for each service drive more activity, thereby reducing waiting lists, but this is not necessarily always effective activity. The introduction of Medicare (publicly funded insurance for older people) in the US fifty years ago was followed by a massive increase in activity by healthcare professionals as they responded to a system that paid a fee for each service provided.

In contrast, in the future, healthcare systems will have to focus on paying or rewarding people for keeping the local population healthy and out of hospital, if at all possible. For example, the changes that are required will have to ensure that primary care teams are rewarded for keeping their diabetic patients in excellent health, rather than the system paying large sums to doctors and hospitals for treating people who develop the complications of poorly controlled diabetes. Insurance systems have always tended to focus on the latter approach; the future for any sustainable healthcare system has to rest on the former.

Another challenge for all of us in the future will be to increase the quality of care we provide for patients, while at the same time dealing with the fact that there will be likely less money available. An integrated health service which has clinical leaders working hand-in-hand with professional managers is essential if we are to provide higher quality care with less money.

In summary, the traditional system of healthcare delivery in Ireland and many other countries was unsustainable from a quality and cost perspective, yet maintaining it was defended vigorously. This book is about the challenge of radically changing how a health system provides its services in order to improve care for patients. The reader must be tempted to ask why we are still only on this journey of change. Why are all these changes not already in place? Writing recently in the *British Medical Journal* about the difficulty of reforming health services, Enrico Coiera, from the Australian Institute of Health Innovation, states: 'It is a conundrum and a source of deep frustration that health systems seem so resistant to change.' He goes on to say that

> ...somehow healthcare has come to be constructed so that it is resistant to new policies and practices, even across apparently dissimilar national systems. The struggle that characterizes health reform may not be a function of poorly designed or targeted initiatives. We may instead be seeing what might be called system inertia, which is a tendency for a system to continue to do the same thing irrespective of the changes in circumstances. (2011: 3693)

Genuine reform of healthcare delivery is slow. However, if we keep to the path we are now on, no matter how uphill and rocky it becomes, we will continue to build a service that puts the patient first.

References

Coiera, E. (2011), 'Why System Inertia Makes Health Reform so Difficult', BMJ 2011; 342: d3693.

Department of Finance (2003), *Commission on Financial Management and Control Systems in the Health Services*, Dublin: The Stationery Office.

Department of Health and Children (2006), *A Vision for Change: Report of the Expert Group on Mental Health Policy*, Dublin: The Stationery Office.

Department of Health and Children (2003), *Audit of Structures and Functions in the Health Service*, Dublin: The Stationery Office.

Department of Health and Children (2003), *Report of the National Task Force on Medical Staffing*, Dublin: The Stationery Office.

Department of Health and Children (2002), *Acute Hospital Bed Capacity, A National Review*, Dublin: The Stationery Office.

Department of Health and Children (2001), *Primary Care: A New Direction*, Dublin: The Stationery Office.

Department of Health and Children (2001), *Quality and Fairness – A Health System for You*, Dublin: The Stationery Office.

Kellermann, A.L. and Martinez., R. (2011), 'The ER, 50 Years On', N Eng J Med, 364: 2278–2279.

National Cancer Forum and Department of Health and Children (2006), *A Strategy for Cancer Control in Ireland*, Dublin: Government Publications.

PA Consulting Group and the Health Service Executive (2007), *Acute Hospital Bed Capacity Review: A Preferred Health System in Ireland 2020*, London: PA Knowledge Limited.

Teamwork Management Services Ltd and the Health Service Executive (2006), *Improving Safety in Achieving Better Standards – An Action Plan for Health Services in the North East*.

Index